A Scientist of Two Worlds

Louis Agassiz, as teacher in America

A SCIENTIST
OF TWO WORLDS:
Louis Agassiz

BY

Catherine Owens Peare

J. B. LIPPINCOTT COMPANY
PHILADELPHIA AND NEW YORK

ACKNOWLEDGMENTS

The author wishes to express her appreciation to the following individuals for their specialized assistance:

Georg Zappler, Paleontologist and Researcher at the American Museum of Natural History, New York

Marcel A. Scherler, Vice Consul, Consulate General of Switzerland, New York

Francisco Medaglia, Director, Brazilian Government Trade Bureau, New York

Dr. Georges Canguilhem, Professor of the History of Sciences at the Sorbonne, Paris

Dr. Alfred S. Romer, Director of the Museum of Comparative Zoology at Harvard University, Cambridge

Dr. Willard J. Jacobson, Associate Professor of Natural Sciences, Teachers College, Columbia University, New York

The author is also grateful to the following for permission to quote from the works indicated:

Houghton Mifflin Company, Boston
  Louis Agassiz, His Life and Correspondence by Elizabeth Cary Agassiz, 1885
  Letters and Recollections of Alexander Agassiz by G. R. Agassiz, 1913
  The Face of the Fields by Dallas Lore Sharp, 1911
Macmillan Company, Ltd., London
  Life, Letters, and Works of Louis Agassiz by Jules Marcou, 1896

Acknowledgments

Radcliffe College, Cambridge
  Elizabeth Cary Agassiz by Lucy Allen Paton, 1919
Cornell University Press, Ithaca
  Louis Agassiz as a Teacher by Lane Cooper, 1917
Librairie Payot, Lausanne
  L'Hôtel des Neuchâtelois, Un Épisode de la Conquête des Alpes, 1928
The Scientific Monthly, Washington
  "Louis Agassiz, Teacher" by David Starr Jordan, November, 1923

Other material has been quoted from:

  Lake Superior: Its Physical Character, Vegetation and Animals by Louis Agassiz, 1850
  A Journey in Brazil by Professor and Mrs. Louis Agassiz, 1868

CONTENTS

1

ANIMALS, PLANTS, AND MINERALS

"THE ice will hold," insisted the older brother.

"Maybe not!" protested the younger, looking out across the frozen lake.

"I'm sure it will be all right. Don't you want to go to the fair?"

Five-year-old Auguste nodded, but added solemnly, "It's very far."

"Only two miles."

"I think it is more."

"Maybe just a little more. Father is over there, and we can drive back around the lake with him in the sleigh."

Seven-year-old Louis Agassiz had his way. He and his brother started to skate across the Lake of Morat toward the town of Morat on the opposite side. The boys were sturdy, and they skated well, and so they ought to have made it across without mishap. But as they were gliding along hand-in-

9

hand they came suddenly to a wide crack in the ice. Auguste began to whimper.

"Don't be afraid," said Louis. "We can get across. I won't let you fall in."

Thereupon he flopped down on his stomach and stretched himself across the crack in the ice.

"Now crawl over on top of me," he told his brother.

Auguste obeyed, trying not to notice the blue-green water beneath him, or the way Louis seemed to sag. At last he was over, scrambling to his feet, helping Louis up.

They took hands and were gliding along once more. Morat was very close. But as they climbed up the bank, they were greeted by the angry voice of one of the men from their village.

"Boys!" he growled. "What were you thinking of? Your mother is frantic. Come!"

He took each boy by the hand and started back across the lake with them.

"I'm tired! I'm tired! I can't skate so far," Louis and Auguste cried at once. "And there's a crack."

"That is just too bad." And he skated with them all the way back. "Now take off your skates," he ordered as soon as they were on land again. "We must hurry home."

They found their mother standing in front of the house, surrounded by a crowd of children. She was holding a telescope in her hand, and they realized that she had seen the whole thing.

Thanking the man who had brought them home, Rose Agassiz shooed her two sons into the house.

"Stay indoors until after luncheon," she told them.

Louis took off his warm outer clothing and wandered upstairs. He strolled to one of the windows and looked out.

Animals, Plants, and Minerals

This was where his mother must have stood with her telescope. Even without one he could see the whole frozen lake, and in the distance beyond the lake rose the mighty peaks of the Alps, so tall that their tips wore snow caps the whole year round. He watched a horse and sleigh trot by the house, its bells tinkling. He really understood why his mother fussed over himself and his brother so much. Her first four children had died, and she didn't want to lose any more.

Jean Louis Rodolphe Agassiz had been born in this house on May 28, 1807. It looked very like every other house in the little Swiss village of Môtier that clustered beside the lake at the foot of the hill called Mount Vully. It had a sharp-gabled roof full of chimneys, and it stood on the land side of the street, facing the lake. What did make the Agassiz house different was the fact that it was the parsonage. The elder Louis Agassiz was the Protestant pastor of Môtier and three other neighboring villages.

Young Louis wandered to his room, the one that he shared with so many live pets. He could not remain downcast very long when he was with any kind of living creature. Tenderly he lifted one of his field mice out of its cage and set it on the floor, stroking the soft fur with the tip of one finger. A knock on the door alarmed him.

"Be careful where you walk," he called. "The mice are free."

Mrs. Agassiz only poked her head in, and he was glad to see that she was smiling.

"How are the birds?" she asked, nodding toward a piece of pine tree standing in a corner, where some wild birds perched.

"They're growing tamer," he told her.

11

A Scientist of Two Worlds

There were some brown cocoons hanging on one of the branches, and she said, "Aren't you afraid the warm room will make the butterflies come out too soon?"

"Oh, no!" he told her. "They know when it is spring. But they aren't butterflies, Mother; they're moths."

"Very well," she said. "Put the mice back in their cage and come to the table."

He obeyed, closing the door cautiously behind him.

In spite of all his care, an occasional tragedy did occur to one or another of his pets. Some time later a friend came into his room suddenly, and before Louis could shout a warning one of his birds was crushed beneath the door. He was grief-stricken for a while, but only for a while. His natural good nature always won out. He cried easily, but he laughed just as easily, and a lot more often.

As soon as the warm air and sun of spring melted the snow from the ground and the ice from the lake, Louis was down at the lakeside begging for rides with the fishermen in their small boats. Jovially one or another always took him aboard, because they enjoyed this bubbling and eager young fellow.

"I must have some live fishes for my aquarium," he explained. "I must have as many kinds as possible."

They knew that. They knew, too, that he could recognize more kinds of fishes than anyone else in Môtier.

When the fishermen brought him back, he carried his fishes home to the garden in back of the house. There a natural spring flowed constantly into a large stone basin fashioned from a granite boulder, and in it Louis Agassiz placed his slippery pets.

Louis and Auguste were both expert fishermen themselves, and they often went fishing along the edge of the lake or up the swift mountain brooks that fed the lake. They knew the

Animals, Plants, and Minerals

favorite haunts of every fish and its habits as well.

Spring in Switzerland meant more than fishing. It meant going on long hikes through the nearby Jura Mountains. The Jura range is not so tall as the Alps, and in summer loses its snow. The range is craggy and wild and full of interesting trails that wind through pine forests or along high ledges.

Hiking meant much more than fresh air and sport to Louis Agassiz, because he was forever collecting specimens of plant and animal life. Rocks interested him as much as live things, and he often returned from a hike bent over double under a sack full of rock specimens.

The Agassiz boys were as sturdy as iron from all the exercise, mountain air, and farm food, and as they grew older they were able to hike farther and farther. Louis in particular was strong and full of energy all his life.

Sometimes their hikes took the Agassiz boys to Cudrefin, another Swiss village about five miles west of Môtier, on the shore of Lake of Neuchâtel. In Cudrefin lived a whole houseful of relatives: Mrs. Agassiz's parents, Dr. and Mrs. Mayor, and several uncles, aunts, and cousins. Grandfather Mayor was a busy country doctor, but he always had time to go fishing with his grandsons.

Louis and Auguste played together, hiked together, fished together, and went to school together. Their father was the local schoolmaster in addition to being a minister. Mr. Agassiz loved books and loved to teach, and he presented his lessons with so much happy enthusiasm that the children enjoyed learning. Louis was a brilliant lad who learned easily; he was as quiet and studious indoors as he was bursting with energy out of doors. He could sit still for hours over a book or a specimen.

The brothers were separated for the first time when Louis

was ten. Since he was the older, he went away to boarding school first, in the town of Bienne, still only twenty miles from home. Bienne, on the northern edge of the Lake of Bienne, was larger than Môtier, and, what pleased Louis most, it was in the heart of the Jura, built up the side of its steep slopes. In spite of nine hours of classes each day, Louis Agassiz had time and energy for exploring the Jura.

Languages were an important part of his studies, because in Europe where countries are small and close together everyone must speak two or three languages to get along. French was Louis Agassiz's native tongue, since he lived in the French-speaking section of Switzerland, and he soon learned to speak German fluently. Greek and Latin were considered an essential part of education, and many hours were given to them. Textbooks were scarce, and the boys at Bienne wrote their lessons in blank copybooks which they saved from year to year.

Louis Agassiz really enjoyed his studies and his life at boarding school, but he enjoyed it more during his second year when Auguste came to join him. Even though they could not have classes together, they could live together, and go home for holidays together—on foot.

One big holiday was just after Easter when their house— there were now two younger Agassiz children, Louis's sisters Olympe and Cecile—the village streets, the church, everywhere, seemed to swarm with young people, dressed in their best. They crowded into the church. Later they held races and contests for colored Easter eggs, and the day ended with a dance in the village square.

Then the twenty miles back to school. But soon there would be another holiday. Môtier was in the grape-growing region, and the gathering of the grapes called for an elaborate

Animals, Plants, and Minerals

festival. There would be great crowds of happy Swiss gathered around the inn tables in the evening singing folk songs.

"The twenty miles home are always shorter than the twenty miles to school," the Agassiz brothers agreed.

In the four years that he spent at Bienne, Louis Agassiz grew from a boy to a young adult. His figure became stocky, though not overly tall, and his hair was brown. He had a kindly, warm, and outgoing disposition, and an endless supply of cheerfulness. Yet, he was extremely sensitive as well, and his eyes could fill with tears at a jibe.

"Oh," his brother prodded him one day, "I know what is the matter with you. You are in love, and I hope it never happens to me."

It was true. Louis was in love with one of his Mayor cousins.

"Be of good cheer," Auguste went on in his mocking tone, "we go home on a holiday tomorrow and you will be united with your true love."

"We must start early," said Louis.

Louis strode along the road at a rapid pace, and they arrived home late in the afternoon.

"Your sisters have gone to Cudrefin to visit with the Mayors," they were told.

Excellent! was Louis's conclusion, and he started out in the direction of Cudrefin.

"We have walked far enough for one day," protested Auguste.

"You, maybe; but not I."

As soon as the Lake of Neuchâtel came into sight in the distance Louis began to run. All of the girls were in swimming, and Louis, to make a terrific impression, dived right

15

into the lake with his clothes on and swam toward them. Auguste just shook his head.

Back at school, when they were undressing for the night, Auguste suddenly shouted at Louis, "What's that on your arm?"

"Her name!" said Louis in a low serious tone. He had used sulphuric acid to tattoo his arm.

"But it's red and swollen!"

It was indeed, and it grew so bad it required medical treatment. He had to go about with his arm in bandages for three weeks, and he took plenty of ribbing for it.

School life, with its long hours of study, its jibes, its sports, and its love affairs, drew to a close when Louis Agassiz was fifteen. He knew what his parents' plans for him were, and he knew they were sensible plans. He was to be apprenticed in the business office of his uncle, François Mayor in Neuchâtel. But the more he thought of a career in the world of bookkeeping and voucher slips, the more he realized that that was not what he wanted to do with his life. He longed for a world of books and scholars, of learning, observing, wondering, discovering new ideas, and writing. He loved the out-of-doors and nature, and he loved all living things—loved to investigate their structure and their habits. All this meant more schooling than his parents could afford.

"I should like," he wrote in one of his copybooks, "to serve my apprenticeship in commerce at Neuchâtel for a year and a half. Then I should like to pass four years at a university in Germany, and finally finish my studies at Paris, where I would stay about five years. Then, at the age of twenty-five, I could begin to write."

Ten more years of training? A bold ambition for the son of a country parson! He did not put it to his father in quite so bold and sweeping a manner, but rather appealed to him

Animals, Plants, and Minerals

and his mother for more schooling—two years perhaps.

His father had chosen a scholarly life, and his mother was the daughter of a physician. They were both willing to listen to their oldest son when he told them he wanted to continue his studies. When they asked him what college he had in mind, he answered at once, "The College of Lausanne."

"We'll manage somehow," they told him. "You may have two years at the College of Lausanne."

Actually, most of his family were willing to understand. The fact that he had an uncle, Dr. Mathias Mayor, living in Lausanne pleased them; and one of his uncles in Cudrefin contributed some funds. To make the two years at Lausanne even happier, Auguste was to go, too.

Lausanne proved a greater experience than Louis Agassiz could have hoped for or imagined. It was the largest city he had seen up to that time. The Lausanne of his day is the old part of town now, with narrow winding streets, tall narrow prim houses built along the side of the Jura range on three levels. Agassiz and his brother could climb the steep cobblestone streets to a point high behind the city and look down upon its Gothic cathedral, its castle, the rooftops of its wealthy homes and small cottages, and below it all the shimmering surface of Lake of Geneva where white sails skimmed by. Beyond Lake of Geneva on its southern shore were the towering Alps. In the countryside near the lake they could see vineyards and flocks of white sheep in pastures.

The Agassiz boys boarded in a private home in town, since there were no dormitories then, and walked to their classes in language, mathematics, philosophy, and—to Louis's great joy—natural science. It was his first taste of that study. There was a real thrill in finding that a subject like zoology was taught in school. The college had a natural history museum—again Agassiz's first—and he went there often. As he looked at the insect collection arranged according to kinds and types in relation to one another, an idea was stimulated in the back of his mind. It was just the beginning of an idea, but one that would grow. There was a plan in nature, he could tell, even from so modest a collection. He soon discovered something else: the top scientists of the day did not agree on how plants and animals ought to be classified. Knowledge about the world of nature was far from complete.

His Uncle Mathias, a prominent physician, was watching this young man, watching him with considerable interest. He took Louis Agassiz into his own laboratory and gave him some beginning lessons in anatomy. They had long conversations together.

And young Agassiz made other scientific friends in Lausanne. One of the most important was Jean de Charpentier who was director of the salt mines in nearby Bex.

With his new courses in science and his new scientific friendships stimulating him, Louis Agassiz could no longer think of a commercial career. He must go on with science. Dr. Mathias Mayor agreed. He could not bear to see Louis Agassiz's talents wasted in an office.

"You must let him study medicine," he advised the boy's parents.

Deep in his heart, Louis Agassiz didn't want to study medicine. He wanted to be a naturalist, but he knew that that was scarcely a career for a poor man's son. He said nothing, though; and shrewdly he thought to himself: "If I am a country doctor, I can study nature as I drive around visiting my patients."

He began his study of medicine at the Medical School of Zurich in 1824, when he was seventeen, and again Auguste

Animals, Plants, and Minerals

went with him. He was moving farther out into the world, to a still larger city, to a wider circle of scientific friends, to more class hours of science.

Zurich is in the German-speaking section of Switzerland, and so all of their lectures were in German. The brothers were glad they had been required to learn German so thoroughly at Bienne.

Louis Agassiz, by now full grown, handsome, brilliant, endowed with a genial and lovable personality, attracted attention at once. His professors particularly noticed the keen young scholar. The professor of natural history took him under his wing, and the same thing happened in geology.

Agassiz discovered in Zurich that there were vast areas of nature to be studied—fishes, land animals, birds, plants, rocks —waiting for him indoors in books and outdoors in their original state. The more he studied, the more he realized that nature was out-of-doors and that most of her still waited to be discovered. As far as nature went he worried less and less about the high cost of books that did not contain the answers he wanted anyway. A true naturalist must hold the live bird in his own hands, must dissect the fish himself, must scale the forbidding mountain peak and test its rocky sides with his own pick and hammer.

He and Auguste did that very thing again and again. Zurich is in the northern Alps, near the region of Switzerland made famous by William Tell, and near some of the most beautiful scenes in the whole country.

"The Righi is only about twenty miles from here," they were told.

"Oh, yes!" declared a student. "The Righi is nearly six thousand feet high. From the top of that mountain you can see half of Switzerland."

A Scientist of Two Worlds

The Agassiz brothers needed only to look at one another and grin, and the decision to climb the Righi on their first free day was made. The Righi, between Lake Lucerne and Lake Zoug, would be their first mountain peak. They started early in the morning with a group of hikers, and after four hours of steady climbing they had reached only the halfway mark. They were high enough, though, to have a wide view of Lake Lucerne and the green plain around it and the city of Lucerne. Now and again they met a shepherd boy or heard the sound of an Alpine horn, or they heard the tinkling of bells tied to the necks of cattle or goats. They trudged along the winding and upward slanting path, up, up, and the higher they went the wider their vista of the countryside became. At last they reached the top, where they planned to spend the night.

"Look at the sky!" said Louis Agassiz. It was a clear blue. "Look, look, look!" was all he could say.

The world spread around them far below and far away. There was Lake Lucerne, looking very small. There were rivers winding through fertile plains and getting lost in forests. To the southwest stretched the snow-capped Bernese Alps, the mighty Jungfrau standing out, all beginning to turn pink in the sunset. To the east were miles of mountains and valleys, villages, winding ribbons of rivers, lakes, and there to the north was Lake Zoug. Their attention was soon drawn to Lake Lucerne, where a black storm was gathering. Mother Nature could really create amazing affects! The storm was far below them, while above their heads the sky was still blue.

Soon after dark Auguste rolled up in his blanket like the others and went to sleep. But Louis remained awake for a long time, watching the storm spend itself and disappear,

Animals, Plants, and Minerals

watching the stars overhead, and gazing out over the vast panorama all around him.

Perhaps it was the dramatic and beautiful scenery of Switzerland that gave Louis Agassiz his happy disposition and his tremendous imagination. It certainly must have helped.

After two years at Zurich, Louis and his brother at last had to part company, because Louis went on to Germany to take courses at Heidelberg and Munich, and Auguste went home to a commercial career in Neuchâtel. It was the custom in Europe then to complete one's medical studies in two or three or even more universities. The Medical School at Zurich did not offer all the courses that Louis needed.

"I have a room in the home of a tobacco merchant," Louis wrote home to his father from Heidelberg. "My windows overlook the town, and my prospect is bounded by a hill situated to the north of Heidelberg. At the back of the house is a large and fine garden, at the foot of which is a very pretty summerhouse. There are also several clumps of trees in the garden, and an aviary filled with native birds. . . ."

His daily schedule was heavy now that he was at a university. He rose at six and was listening to his first lecture by seven, and his entire morning was spent either in classrooms or in the laboratory dissecting specimens. He dined at one and took a long, brisk walk in the fresh air. Then, back to his own room to study until five. He attended another lecture at five, took another walk, ate dinner, and returned to his room for more study until nine o'clock at night.

"Then," he told his father, "I go to the Swiss Club, or, if I am tired, to bed."

If he was tired! Only Louis Agassiz could have said *if;*

any other student would have been exhausted long before nine.

He reveled in his new subjects: zoology, botany, anatomy, chemistry, the use of the microscope. And there were thousands of books in the University library.

The most important thing in Heidelberg was the University. It was the most famous in Europe, and had been for hundreds of years. In Heidelberg, as in many German universities, the students lived in complete freedom, boarding where they pleased. They attended their lectures when and if they pleased, some in the school's one and only building, others in halls about town. The students were the most important citizens in the town, sauntering and swaggering about with a devil-may-care manner, singing traditional songs, swarming in and out of the beer gardens. They wore a special kind of costume: a sack-like coat, a shirt with its collar wide open, britches and high jack boots; they smoked pipes with three-foot stems and let their hair grow long down their necks. There was only one important sport at the German universities, and that was duelling—with swords.

The friendly Agassiz soon fitted himself into the life of a Heidelberg student, fencing and all. He was known before long as the best swordsman in town, and he used his talent to defend the reputation of his Swiss Club. Usually the young men belonged to one club or another, and Agassiz's club, of which he was president, claimed that the German club had "insulted" them. It was a case of any excuse for a sword match, and the Swiss delivered their challenge.

"Very well," the Germans replied. "We will send our best swordsman to meet yours."

"Indeed!" replied Agassiz. "I did not challenge *one* of you. I shall take you all on, one after another."

Animals, Plants, and Minerals

There was little danger of being killed. The combatants wore several thicknesses of clothing, wrapped yards of cloth around their necks, covered their sword arms, and wore wide leather girdles. Oh, perhaps a saber cut on the face, but that only marked one for a university man in later life.

The moment of the affair was tense. A crowd of men formed a circle around Agassiz and his first opponent. They took their positions and began. In a very short while Agassiz had finished off four opponents and was starting on his fifth, when the German club surrendered.

Agassiz was popular and well liked, and among the many friends that he made at Heidelberg two were particularly important. One was Karl Schimper; the other was Alexander Braun. The three, although different personalities, had a great deal in common. They all loved science, especially natural science. They were all striving for new knowledge that had not yet been discovered. Both Braun and Schimper were to become prominent botanists, while Agassiz grew more engrossed in zoology. They lived together, worked together, did almost everything together, and helped one another grow and develop.

Karl Schimper was irritable and quick tempered with tight-strung nerves. Sometimes his attitude toward life was downright sour. Agassiz and Braun did not let that bother them. They knew that Schimper was a great man underneath it all and that he had had many hardships in his past to make him that way.

To know Alexander Braun was to know his whole family, who lived in the town of Karlsruhe. Both Heidelberg and Karlsruhe were in the Duchy of Baden. Today Baden is a province of Germany, but then it was an independent state, called a Duchy because it was ruled by a prince with the rank of duke. In times of war the Duchy of Baden usually turned to the stronger state of Prussia to the north.

Alexander Braun's father was Postmaster General of Baden, but his real interest was science. From the day that Alexander Braun met Louis Agassiz he wanted him to join his family circle.

"Come home with me," he insisted. "Come home with me and spend your vacation at Karlsruhe."

Agassiz accepted, and Braun wrote happily to his father, "I bring to you one who knows every fish which passes under the bridge, every bird which flies above our heads, every insect which crawls in the grass, every plant which grows on our mountainside."

Karlsruhe was some thirty-five miles south of Heidelberg, nearly a day's journey in a horse-drawn carriage. As the carriage left Heidelberg, Louis Agassiz looked back. They were driving out over a plain and behind them was the ridge of the green mountain against which Heidelberg was built. The Neckar River flowed out of a narrow gorge in the mountains and wound through the town, then across the open land toward the Rhine.

When the carriage was still at least three miles from Karlsruhe, the road began to be lined on each side with an endless column of poplar trees. They could scarcely see the town when they reached it, because it seemed buried in poplars. Karlsruhe was the capital of Baden, and its castle, the home of the ruling prince, stood in the center of town. The principal streets radiated out from its park like spokes of a wheel. Agassiz thought that it was an exceptionally lovely town with so many palatial buildings, such clean streets, and lovely promenades and parks. How different Germany was from Switzerland!

Animals, Plants, and Minerals

The Braun home faced the park that surrounded the ducal palace. From its windows Agassiz could see flower gardens and groves, and at night could hear nightingales singing.

"There are botanical gardens and greenhouses in the royal park," Alex told him.

The Braun house itself was big enough to be called a palace. It had its own huge gardens. The wing of the house that was surrounded by the garden was two stories high; the second floor contained bedrooms for guests, the first floor was taken up with laboratories, scientific books, and collections of dried plants, minerals, preserved animals.

There were six Brauns: Mr. and Mrs. Braun, two sons Alexander and Maximilian, and two daughters Cecile and Emmy. The Brauns were cultured and charming and interested in all manner of things. Cecile's particular talent was drawing; Emmy's was music. No wonder they watched eagerly for the carriage that was bringing them the summer guest who knew "every fish . . . every bird . . . every insect . . . every plant . . ."

Louis Agassiz spent the happiest summer of his life, roaming the fields and nearby forests in the daytime with Alexander, Maximilian, and the elder Braun. They collected specimens and brought them back to the laboratory. They spent weeks gathering wild mushrooms and studying their delicate colorings, their structure, their tiny spores, so that they could identify them all. Cecile's artistic talent proved most useful, because she made the drawings of the specimens for them.

Karlsruhe became a second home for Louis Agassiz and he was to spend many of his holidays there. Karl Schimper soon joined the group, and so did Arnold Guyot, a student from Neuchâtel.

A Scientist of Two Worlds

When Agassiz was stricken with typhus fever, after he'd been at Heidelberg about a year, Alex Braun told him firmly, "You are coming to Karlsruhe as soon as you can be moved."

In the big, ample, friendly house Louis Agassiz began to recover rapidly. Cecile was oftenest at his side. He admired her jet black hair, dark eyes, and olive skin. She was slim and rather fragile.

"You look like an artist," he told her.

One day Alex came in and found Louis and Cecile glowing and smiling and holding each other's hands.

"Well?" he asked with a twinkle in his eye.

"We are engaged," they told him.

The Brauns were overjoyed, and they hurried to his room, chattering and laughing.

"Please, please!" said Mr. Braun. "He is still very weak. Do not tire him."

"I think," said Alex, "that by tomorrow he will be strong enough for a stroll in the garden."

"Louis must return to his family in Switzerland, as soon as he is strong enough, and share the good news with them," declared Cecile.

2

LIVING AND FOSSIL FISHES

WHEN Louis was strong enough for the journey, Alexander accompanied him home. Home this time was Orbe, Mr. Agassiz's new parish, the Swiss village just south of the Lake of Neuchâtel. The Agassiz family had moved there about the time that Louis and Auguste had completed their studies at Bienne.

Everyone was happy to have Louis back, happy to learn of his engagement, too, but startled to see how wasted and pale he looked. Mrs. Agassiz particularly seized the chance to mother her big son once more.

At Orbe, so close to the Jura Mountains, where the air is brisk and healthy, Louis Agassiz recovered his strength quickly. He was soon out striding along country roads, picking up this specimen and that. Braun and Schimper had both increased his interest in plant life, and he noticed for the first time how very many kinds of plants there were in the

Jura region. He began to make a dried collection of all the plants he could find. The result was his first scientific article: a descriptive list of plants in the southern Jura.

The extraordinary thing about Louis Agassiz was that he seemed to be able to remember everything he learned, down to the last detail. He was only twenty, and already he knew enough for a dozen men. How could one person hold so much information and keep it in order? That was what his friends and professors wanted to know.

Agassiz had come home to Orbe in June, and August found him back in the home of the Brauns. By the time the air had turned chill and brisk enough for October, he and Alex were on their way to the University of Munich. They had enrolled there to complete their medical courses. They took their time touring through the historic German countryside.

Agassiz wrote his brother Auguste a long letter describing the trip: "From Karlsruhe we traveled post to Stuttgart, where we passed the greater part of the day in the Museum, in which I saw many things quite new to me: a llama, for instance ... You know that this animal lives in South America, where it is to the natives what the camel is to the Arab; that is to say, it provides them with milk, wool, and meat, and is used by them, moreover, for driving and riding. There was a North American buffalo of immense size; also an elephant from Africa, and one from Asia; besides these, a prodigious number of gazelles, deer, cats, and dogs; skeletons of a hippopotamus and an elephant; and lastly the fossil bones of a mammoth—found frozen in a mass of ice in Siberia. . . . You know that the mammoth is no longer found living. . . . There were besides many other kinds of fossil animals. . . ."

And so on to Esslingen, Goeppingen, and Ulm.

Living and Fossil Fishes

"I have never seen anything more beautiful than the view as we left Ulm," Louis told Auguste.

Ulm was a city of three rivers. It stood on the left bank of the Danube with the tiny River Blau flowing through its middle, sixteenth-century houses standing prim at the water's edge, and the Iller River just above the town. There the guilds of the Meistersingers had held their song festivals and contests longer than anywhere else in Europe, and there in another half century after Agassiz's visit Albert Einstein would be born.

After Ulm came Augsburg, a distant view of the Tyrolean Alps, and Munich.

"My address is opposite the Sendlinger Thor No. 37. I have a very pretty chamber on the lower floor with an alcove for my bed. The house is situated outside the town, on a promenade, which makes it very pleasant. Moreover, by walking less than a hundred yards, I reach the Hospital and the Anatomical School—a great convenience for me when the winter weather begins. One thing gives me great pleasure: from one of my windows the whole chain of the Tyrolean Alps is visible as far as Appenzell; and as the country is flat to their very base, I see them better than we see our Alps from the plain. It is a great pleasure to have at least a part of our Swiss mountains always in sight."

Actually he and Braun had their room in the home of one of the science professors. Karl Schimper appeared a few weeks later to join them.

Agassiz was on his usual schedule that would have discouraged a lazy man: seven to nine at the hospital, nine to eleven at the library, eleven to one for lectures, luncheon at one of the cafés, then more lectures until five. "These ended, I take a walk although it is then dark. The environs of

A Scientist of Two Worlds

Munich are covered with snow, and the people have been going about in sleighs these three weeks. When I am frozen through I come home, and set to work to review my lectures of the day, or I write and read till eight or nine o'clock. Then I go to my café for supper. After supper I am glad to return to the house and go to bed." Thus he wrote to his sister Cecile.

But it was not all so grim. There was tea one afternoon a week at the home of Professor Carl von Martius who was conservator of the botanic garden and a botany professor at the University. He and the zoologist, Professor Johann von Spix, had spent three years in Brazil studying its plant and animal life, and he loved to tell the young men about his Brazilian experiences.

On Fridays the three young men went to the Munich fish market and poked around in the barrels and bins for interesting specimens. They passed an evening now and again with one professor or another, and there were holidays in the Alps —and fencing.

Louis Agassiz spent three years at Munich from November, 1827, to December, 1830; and long before the three years were up he had captured the admiration and attention of his professors. Only once in a blue moon, they admitted, did a student like Agassiz come to them. Such scientific insight! Such powers of observation! Such a spirit of dedication!

Before he had completed his first year, Professor von Martius sent for him.

"You know, Agassiz, of my trip to Brazil?"

Agassiz nodded. He had listened openmouthed to it at many afternoon teas.

"Well," Von Martius went on, "perhaps you also know that my associate and collaborator on that trip, Dr. von Spix, died

Living and Fossil Fishes

a short while ago. I am left with a huge task of analyzing, identifying, classifying, and describing the hundreds and hundreds of plant and animal specimens that we brought back with us."

Agassiz's pulse began to race.

"I know, Agassiz, that you know a great deal about fresh-water fishes," and Martius explained that he wanted Agassiz to take the whole collection of Brazilian fishes, classify and identify them, and write a short description of each one. Agassiz was to receive no pay, but he knew how important it would be to publish a scientific work even before he had received his medical degree. So of course he accepted the assignment.

With his usual zeal and painstaking thoroughness he went to work on the collection—all in addition to his regular schoolwork.

But the science of fishes, or ichthyology, was not the practice of human medicine. Agassiz decided not to tell his family about his work on the Brazilian fishes until it was completed and published.

"Various things which I have begun keep me a prisoner here," he wrote mysteriously to his brother. "I have kept it a secret from Papa, too."

Letters traveled back and forth constantly between Agassiz and his parents, his brother and sisters, his fiancée.

In his letters he began to show how disturbed he was by the fact that he really didn't want to be a doctor. He wanted to be a traveling naturalist. By the time he took up the Brazilian fishes, he was discussing the problem with his family.

"You chose the university which offered, as you thought, the most ample means to reach your end; and now, how is it

A Scientist of Two Worlds

that you look forward only with distaste to the practice of medicine?" his mother wrote to him. "Have you reflected seriously before setting aside this profession? Indeed, we cannot consent to such a step."

They were keeping him in school at a considerable sacrifice, she reminded him. Had he forgotten that he was planning to be married? He could not support a family chasing butterflies.

"I have said to myself that I would remain unmarried till my work should assure me a peaceful and happy future," he wrote back to his mother. "You think that I wish to renounce entirely the study of medicine? On the contrary . . . what repels me is the thought of practicing medicine for a livelihood. . . ."

His father wrote him a few pages on the subject: "Begin by reaching your first aim, a physician's and surgeon's diploma. I will not for the present hear of anything else, and that is more than enough."

No wonder Agassiz did not mention the Brazilian project.

"If during the course of my studies I succeed in making myself known by a work of distinction," he hinted to his father very cautiously, "will you not then consent that I shall study, at least during one year, the natural sciences alone, and then accept a professorship of natural history? With the understanding," he added hastily, "that in the first place, and in the time agreed upon, I shall take my doctor's degree?"

The more he worked on the Brazilian fishes, the more he longed to be a traveling naturalist. How many more kinds of fishes were there in Brazilian waters than Spix and Martius had discovered? If he were to do a superb job on these fishes for Martius . . . If the book he turned out attracted a little attention in scientific circles . . . If, if, if . . .

Living and Fossil Fishes

One day when he was alone in the room, Schimper and Braun rushed in and asked excitedly, "Have you heard of Humboldt?"

Alexander von Humboldt? Of course! Who had not heard of Humboldt? Humboldt must be at least sixty. His achievements ranked with the best of living scientists. There was no field of science that Humboldt did not know about: physical geography, rocks, volcanoes, plants, animals, the stars and the planets, the races of man. Above all else, in Agassiz's eyes, Humboldt was a traveling naturalist. He had spent five years in the Western Hemisphere before Agassiz was born, exploring Venezuela, the Orinoco River, Colombia, Ecuador, the Andes Mountains, Peru, Mexico, Cuba, the United States. He had been all over Europe. Humboldt observed, collected specimens, studied, discovered new scientific principles, lectured and wrote about them. Lately he had been in Berlin.

"Humboldt is planning an expedition to central Asia!" said the young men. "Of course he will take students, and we have talked to several of our professors. They will recommend us."

Happy confusion reigned. What if it were too late? What if Humboldt had already chosen the members of his expedition?

Agassiz wrote to his father: "This journey is to last two years, at the end of which time, happily at home once more, I can follow with all desirable facilities the career I have chosen."

The three hopefuls walked on air while they waited for Humboldt's decision. Returning from a professor's home one cold moonlight evening, they strode along talking jovially of their trip to Asia. Agassiz could not contain himself. He flung himself down and rolled along in the snow for pure joy.

In a few weeks the three had to climb down from their cloud and settle back into their studies. Humboldt notified them that he had already chosen what assistants he would need.

In the spring of 1829, when Agassiz had been in Munich about a year and a half, he received a degree of Doctor of Philosophy from the University of Erlangen, a city north of Munich. But his medical degree was still to be achieved.

He was hard at work on the Brazilian fishes, and that same summer he completed the first part of the project. It was written in Latin and dedicated to Georges Cuvier, one of the most outstanding zoologists of his times, a friend of Humboldt.

Cuvier lived in Paris, a scientific center in those days; he believed that the proper way to classify and identify animals was to study their internal structure and compare them with one another. "Comparative anatomy is the only true basis for classifying animals," he insisted. That was his approach to the study of fossil animals, too. It was really Cuvier who created the science of paleontology, which is the study of fossils. So it was quite natural that a young and hopeful scientist like Agassiz, after completing a long task in the comparative anatomy of fishes, should dedicate it to the leading scientist in that field.

Dr. Cuvier had once been a brilliant and promising young science student himself, and he remembered that he had received help from those older than himself. He was deeply interested in education as well. Georges Cuvier read Agassiz's work very carefully and then wrote him a cordial letter: "You

Living and Fossil Fishes

and Monsieur Martius have done me honor in placing my name at the head of a work so admirable as the one you have just published. The importance and the rarity of the species therein described, as well as the beauty of the figures, will make the work an important one in ichthyology, and nothing could heighten its value more than the accuracy of your descriptions."

Louis Agassiz had had a nod of approval from the great Cuvier! He knew well enough how important that was in the field of science. Now he wanted another nod of approval —from his father.

"I hasten, my dear son," wrote his father, "to announce the arrival of your beautiful work, which reached us on Thursday, from Geneva. I have no terms in which to express the pleasure it has given me."

Louis Agassiz realized then, more than ever before, that he was blessed with generous and understanding parents. That fall he took his one and only trip home to Orbe from Munich and spent October and November with his family.

"By spring I shall have my medical degree," he promised his father.

His father looked a little doubtful. There were only twenty-four hours in a day, and Louis had not completed his task for Martius. He was also saying that he planned to begin two other works, one on the fresh-water fishes of Europe, and another on fossil fishes.

"They are all related," Louis explained. "Dr. Cuvier discovered that. He discovered that fossils of ancient fishes buried in earth layers, even though they are extinct, very much resemble present-day fishes."

Paleontology was the study of the fossil remains of ancient fishes, Louis went on to say, and ichthyology was the study of present-day fishes. These were two parts of the same story. "I already know a great deal about the fresh-water fishes of Europe. I've really been studying them all my life." Scattered through the museums of Europe were small collections of fossil fishes; they needed to be brought together into one great study. They needed to be compared and studied. He meant to correspond with other paleontologists as well, to make his work as complete and valuable as possible.

"And there are so many that are still buried in the various layers of the earth's surface that haven't yet been collected," he started to say, but when he saw the expression on his father's face, he added, "I promise you! I promise you that I won't neglect my medical studies. I shall have my degree in the spring. You will see."

He kept his promise to his father. Louis Agassiz, who had the energy of several men, did everything he planned to do when he returned to Munich. He began his own research on fresh-water fishes. He began to study fossil fishes in every museum he could reach: in Munich, Stuttgart, Tübingen, Erlangen, Würzburg, Karlsruhe, Frankfort. He worked like a Trojan on his medical courses and received his medical degree in April 1830. That alone would have been an achievement for a man who was within a few weeks of his twenty-third birthday. But even before he received his medical degree, he ranked with outstanding scientists of his day because of his work on the Brazilian fishes.

He did not go home immediately. Home meant settling down to earning a living as a country doctor. It meant giving up the stimulating company of Braun and Schimper, and doing his work in natural history when he could find the time. So Agassiz remained in Munich for a few more months and continued his research on fossil and fresh-water fishes.

Living and Fossil Fishes

The two books he was planning required careful and accurate illustrations, and just a short while before, he had met the artist, Joseph Dinkel. Dinkel was a naturalist at heart and showed great talent in making a live fish appear just as alive on paper.

"You must not interpret!" Agassiz cautioned him. "You must show each line in the fin, each scale, exactly as it is. You must match the colors perfectly. We cannot use poetic license in a science book."

Dinkel understood, and he agreed to do the color plates for Agassiz's two books.

The optimistic Agassiz, with his great vision, always planned everything as though money grew on trees. He was living from hand to mouth himself when he hired Dinkel, and so he made board and keep a part of the bargain. Dinkel moved in with Agassiz, Schimper, and Braun and shared their bread and beer and tobacco.

"We live very simply," they explained to Dinkel.

"So I see," Dinkel answered good-naturedly.

Agassiz plunged even deeper into his project. He engaged the Stuttgart publisher, M. Cotta, to publish his books. Cotta was more sensible than Agassiz in the matter. He insisted that Agassiz first obtain a list of subscribers so that they could count on selling enough copies of the books at least to pay the cost of publishing.

"Be at ease about me," Louis wrote to his brother Auguste. "I have strings enough to my bow, and need not feel anxious about the future."

He had hoped to finish his books and see them published before returning home, but at the end of the year he was no-where near that goal. He could not delay any longer; he must begin his life as a country doctor.

A Scientist of Two Worlds

"Come with me," he said to Dinkel. "You can live with my family, and we can continue our work together."

This return home was to the Swiss town of Concise, on the shore of Lake of Neuchâtel, the elder Agassiz's newest parish. Louis found his parents quite happy in their Concise home. Every room had a view of the lake, and on the land was a vineyard and fruit orchard.

The arrival of Agassiz and Dinkel and all their boxes and jars filled with specimens caused a great commotion. Louis had warned his family to expect Dinkel. "He is the artist who makes all my drawings. If there is no room for him in the house he can be lodged elsewhere."

There was to be no lodging elsewhere. Eagerly Mr. Agassiz led them upstairs.

"Here is the room we have set aside for you to work in," he told them. "It has a nice view and plenty of light."

The two young men became lost in their work at once.

"How will you pay Dinkel?" Louis's father asked one day. "You cannot expect any more financial help from us or your relatives. You must face facts."

Louis Agassiz did make some effort to build up a medical practice, but his patients were few and far between.

One day an old family friend dropped in for a visit. He was Charles Christinat, another Protestant pastor, who had always had a soft place in his heart for Louis Agassiz. Everyone called him Papa Christinat. After listening carefully and looking over the family situation of the Agassizes, Papa Christinat said to Louis, "Come. Walk with me. I want to talk to you."

They strolled along toward the lake.

"Louis," the older man began, "how many patients have come to you for treatment?"

Living and Fossil Fishes

"Oh, half a dozen or so."

"And the fees they have paid you?"

Agassiz just laughed and said, "When I can complete my work on fossil fishes I hope the book will sell sufficiently to yield me something."

"And your fiancée?"

"She is still waiting, but I am afraid I shall lose her if I dally much longer."

"Agassiz," said Papa Christinat, "if you could wave a magic wand and do as you pleased, what would you do?"

"Oh!" cried Agassiz without a moment's hesitation. "I should go to Paris. I need the material in the museums there, and the greatest naturalists are living in Paris—Humboldt and Cuvier!"

Christinat nodded. "I anticipated this," and he drew a small package from his pocket and laid it in Agassiz's hand. "Here, Agassiz, is money for your trip to Paris, and I happen to know that you will receive a little more help from one of your uncles in Neuchâtel and from your publisher, Cotta."

Agassiz could only stare at the package in his hand.

"But Papa Christinat . . ."

"Enough, enough! I have only one requirement. On your way to Paris, go up to Karlsruhe and see Cecile."

3

PARIS

"STAY with us a few days!" the Brauns pleaded when he and Dinkel arrived in Karlsruhe.

"Yes, Louis," said Cecile. "We've seen so little of you."

The decision to take Dinkel to Paris with him had been quickly made, and the two men had left Concise in September. Not forgetting his family's wishes, Agassiz had stopped off and visited hospitals along the way; and for his own work he had visited museums.

He remained several weeks in Karlsruhe, walking over the countryside in the daytime with Alexander, passing his evenings with Cecile.

"When I have completed my books," he started to say to her.

"Then we shall make plans," she replied happily.

When Karl Schimper heard that Agassiz was in Karlsruhe, he, too, soon appeared on the scene. December was upon them before Agassiz and Dinkel managed to leave for Paris.

As they jounced along in the diligence, their excitement at visiting such a great and famous city began to mount. Neither of them had ever seen Paris before.

"I hope I have a chance to meet Georges Cuvier," Agassiz went on. "I want to tell him about these two new books I am working on."

They fell silent for long periods, but as the diligence neared its destination they leaned out of the windows to watch for a first glimpse of Paris. It seemed incredibly far away. By the time the coach rumbled into a cobble-stoned court, Agassiz and Dinkel were stiff and exhausted from the long ride and dust gritted between their teeth. They stepped out of the diligence into a milling crowd of children and beggars and porters.

"Can you please direct us?" one of them asked.

"Yes, Monsieur?"

"To the rue Copeau?"

"Oh, yes, Monsieur. It is on the other side of the Seine—on the Left Bank—in the Latin Quarter."

Their diligence had deposited them in the northern part of town, and the address they sought was on the southern side.

"I had no idea a city could be so large!" declared Dinkel as they trudged along.

The Seine, they quickly discovered, curves through the center of Paris from east to west. They found their way across one of its bridges to the Left Bank and were soon located in the cheap little boarding house where they planned to stay, Number 4 rue Copeau. That night they simply washed, ate, and fell on their beds. But next morning their strength was restored and they began to explore. Not only

A Scientist of Two Worlds

were their quarters and meals cheap, but they were in the heart of the neighborhood where they would be working.

"The medical school is within ten minutes' walk; the Botanical Garden is not two hundred steps away; and the hospital is just opposite," Agassiz wrote to his father.

He had to make every minute in Paris count, because Papa Christinat's money would not last forever, and so he embarked on one of his heavy schedules: hospital clinic early, breakfast at ten, then to the Museum of Natural History to work on fossil fishes until dark, next, supper, then more study and work. Dinkel labored diligently over his illustrations.

Everything had to be fitted in somehow, one thing in particular—making the acquaintance of the man to whom his work on Brazilian fishes had been dedicated: Georges Cuvier.

Professor Cuvier was just as eager to meet Agassiz, and on his second day in Paris an invitation came from the learned gentleman to pay him a call. Agassiz hurried to the address.

Cuvier turned out to be tall and quite fat, and because he was nearsighted he had the habit of bending forward and peering at the person he was talking to. He was cordial, though, and eager to help his young visitor.

"Come in, Agassiz. Come in," and he looked hard at the large bundle that Agassiz was carrying.

As soon as they sat down, Agassiz showed Cuvier its contents: some of the text of his new book on fossil fishes and Dinkel's delicately colored illustrations.

"How much is there?" asked Cuvier.

"I have completed a hundred and seventy-one pages of manuscript," Agassiz told him, "and Dinkel is keeping pace with his illustrations."

"Good, good! You know? I have started another work

myself. I hope I live long enough to complete it. It is to be called *The Natural History of Living Fishes.* In it I hope to describe at least five thousand species of fishes and show how they are all related to one another."

Agassiz found it hard to remember that Cuvier was sixty-two, because his mind was so young and so full of imagination. Soon he was visiting with Cuvier every Saturday evening, and on one of those evenings Cuvier handed him a pile of material.

"Here," he said. "These are the drawings and notes that my assistant made while I was studying the collections of fossil fishes at the British Museum and other places. You are welcome to use them." He had thought of doing a work on fossil fishes himself, he said, but after seeing Agassiz's work had changed his mind.

Tenderly Agassiz took the precious material back to his room.

Another time Cuvier said, "You must meet Humboldt," and soon took him to Humboldt's quarters.

Agassiz found Humboldt to be a very different person from Cuvier. He was the same age as Cuvier, but there the similarity ended. Where Cuvier was handsome, Humboldt's appearance was spoiled by a big nose and smallpox scars on his forehead, and Humboldt could suddenly come out with an insult that cut to the bone. Plenty of people were terrified of Humboldt.

But to Agassiz none of this mattered. Humboldt was his dream of a traveling naturalist; Humboldt had been absolutely everywhere. Agassiz's charm won the day with Humboldt, and Humboldt began to keep an eye on the twenty-four-year-old scientist who showed such amazing talent.

A Scientist of Two Worlds

One day Agassiz answered a knock on his door and was startled to discover that Humboldt had come to pay him a visit. As Humboldt walked in and looked around, Agassiz suddenly realized how tiny and crowded and poverty-stricken his room looked. Humboldt didn't seem to mind. All that interested him was Agassiz's bookshelf.

There was a copy of Aristotle's *Zoology*. Fine, fine! And there was one of Linnaeus's books. Excellent! Linnaeus was the great Swedish botanist who had created the system for identifying plants. And there was Cuvier's *Animal Kingdom*. Excellent! Cuvier had a fine perspective on the whole animal kingdom. But then Humboldt's finger pointed to a twelve-volume encyclopedia.

"What are you doing with this ass's bridge?" he demanded.

That was his way. It didn't occur to Agassiz to take offense. He was thrilled to realize that Humboldt had faith in him.

"Let us have luncheon together," Humboldt said another time, and Agassiz sat spellbound, scarcely eating a mouthful, while Humboldt told him of his adventures with electric fishes in Venezuela.

The days in Paris flew by. Agassiz and Dinkel tried never to waste a minute. They wanted to finish the books before Agassiz's money gave out. It *was* giving out, though, and Agassiz began to realize that he would have to consider giving up Dinkel. Dinkel realized it, too.

Just as their money was about gone, an envelope arrived in the mail. It contained a thousand francs—from Humboldt! One glance at that tiny room and Humboldt had guessed what the situation was. He had then queried Agassiz's publisher, Cotta, and found that Agassiz had practically no money at all.

"My benefactor and friend," Agassiz wrote at once to

Paris

Humboldt. "It is too much; I cannot find words to tell you how deeply your letter of today has moved me . . . At what a moment does your help come to me! I inclose a letter from my dear mother that you may understand my whole position. My parents will now readily consent that I should devote myself entirely to science, and I am freed from the distressing thought that I may be acting contrary to their wishes and their will. But they have not the means to help me, and have proposed that I should return to Switzerland and give lessons either in Geneva or Lausanne."

Louis's family had given up the hope of having a doctor for a son, and they were trying to help him with other practical suggestions for supporting himself—and Cecile. Yes, the idea had occurred to him to teach. Teaching was a real possibility. By that he meant teaching natural science, of course.

"I think you would make a fine teacher," said Alexander Braun who had finally followed Agassiz to Paris.

The lure of the great city with its fine museums was more than Braun could resist once he began to think of his best friend working and living there.

"But first," Braun insisted, "finish your books. They are going to be important to everyone."

Braun added his encouragement to everyone else's. He, like Humboldt and Cuvier, wanted to see Agassiz's books completed, because he knew they would be so valuable. Thus, Agassiz's life in Paris was as filled with stimulating friendships as his life at Munich and his holidays at Karlsruhe had been.

Braun looked after him better than anyone, since he had his sister's interest in mind.

"You know," Braun said with a grin one spring day, "you

45

are closer to the seashore than you have ever been in your life before."

Agassiz's imagination was on fire at once. Braun was right. He had never seen the ocean. He had never investigated salt-water animals and plants.

"How long can we spend at the seashore?"

"Two or three days."

"We can stretch it to five, if we are economical."

One brisk, gray March day, Agassiz, Braun and Dinkel set out for Normandy. They explored all along the French coast from Le Havre to Dieppe. They had only five days, but Agassiz made them a great five. He had tapped a whole new department of nature, had seen tiny animals, so many kinds that he had not seen before! He had held seaweed in his hands, felt its slippery fronds, opened their swollen repro-ductive sacs.

"At last I have looked upon the sea and its riches!" he declared at the end of his brief holiday.

And so back to Paris and his ancient and modern fishes and his conversations with Humboldt and Cuvier. But his con-versations with Cuvier were not to go on much longer. That same spring an epidemic of cholera was taking its toll all over Europe, especially in Paris, and it struck Georges Cuvier. He was making a speech before the Chamber of Peers, of which he was a member, when he collapsed. Scarcely had his friends recovered from their surprise and panic when they received the news, "Cuvier is dead."

"But he was only sixty-three!" Agassiz, Dinkel and Braun said to one another. "He still had great work to do!"

They talked far into the night of Cuvier's achievements, his wisdom, the recognition he had received, the contribu-tions to science that he had made. Once he had given Louis

Paris

Agassiz some very sage advice, when he saw the long hours that Agassiz was putting in. "Be prudent," he said, "and remember that too much work kills."

Agassiz paid little heed at the time. He went right on working, ignoring the strain that he felt in his eyes when he used the microscope. He simply had to finish his work in Paris so that he would be free to accept a teaching post when one was offered to him.

He had been writing letters of application to schools in several cities, and thus many people in the world of science knew he was looking for work. They also knew that the great Cuvier had thought very highly of Agassiz. Offers began to come in, one for a post that Cuvier himself had once held. Cuvier's publishers even asked Agassiz to collaborate with Cuvier's assistant in finishing Cuvier's book on the *Natural History of Living Fishes*. All these offers were tempting. So was one that he received from the town of Neuchâtel to be a professor of natural history at its Lyceum, a kind of preparatory school.

Agassiz was troubled. He loved Switzerland, and he wanted a teaching post. The teaching post would give him the time and opportunity to finish his own books. He decided to talk it over with Dr. Humboldt.

"What shall I do?" he asked. "These positions in Paris may lead to bigger things."

"Do not become involved in these busy jobs here in Paris, Agassiz," said Humboldt. "Your own book is nearing completion. Finish it. It is needed. You want to teach. Then take the teaching post."

Agassiz nodded and said nothing.

"I know," said Humboldt, "that the salary they are offering you in Neuchâtel is pitifully small. But you will move up and up to better teaching posts, to a university professorship some day. You are still in your twenties. You can afford to be patient."

Agassiz agreed, and, to the satisfaction of everyone who had his best interest at heart, he accepted the job at the Lyceum. In the autumn of 1832 he set out for Neuchâtel.

4

NEUCHÂTEL

VERY few people had ever heard of the town of Neuchâtel when Louis Agassiz went there to teach. There were many towns just like it. It stood on the western edge of the Lake of Neuchâtel, some of its houses on the narrow shore, some of them along steep streets up the slope of the Jura Mountains. It was the chief town of the principality of Neuchâtel, governed by the King of Prussia, and not yet part of Switzerland. The mountains were covered with forests and the valleys were full of vineyards. Almost directly across the lake on the eastern shore was Cudrefin, home of Agassiz's grandparents.

On the day that Agassiz began to talk to his first class, Neuchâtel began to change. The sleepy, obscure place began to stir and wake up. In a very few months it was a humming scientific center and almost everyone in town was Louis Agassiz's pupil.

A Scientist of Two Worlds

When Louis Agassiz stepped into the classroom he stepped into his own, because he was a born teacher. He loved sharing knowledge with others. He loved to stimulate curiosity. It thrilled him to be surrounded by bubbling young people while he explained the gills of a fish, the wings of a grasshopper, the stamens of a flower, the colorings of a rock.

"All life, all nature, is one," he told them. "These details are all related. They are part of one great plan, and God is the author of all."

And the plan was out-of-doors, not in a classroom, not in books. He took his pupils on field trips along the edge of the lake, up beside tumbling mountain streams, or into the mountains of the Jura. They must do their own collecting, their own discovering, their own learning.

"The environment in which an animal lives is an important part of his life story," he would say.

If he led them alongside of a swift mountain stream to show them the fishes who made it their home, he gave them a lesson in geology at the same time. The stream was working to wash the mountain down into the lake. Or with his geological hammer he would crack away a piece of cliff, then break it apart in his hand. Perhaps he would uncover a tiny shell buried in the rock, a coiled shell of a little Mollusk, once a living animal called an ammonite, now extinct, but related to present-day Mollusks.

"When my book on fossil fishes comes out, you will learn in it that in this very region of Neuchâtel in the Jura a fossil fish was found—one of the Pycnodonts, a very primitive fish that is extinct, a flat, wide fellow who swam vertically, one of those heavy-scaled fishes called Ganoids."

His students would look at him wonderingly. He wanted them to wonder.

Neuchâtel

"Now!" he would go on. "How do you suppose a fish ever found his way to the top of this mountain and buried himself in the rock layers?"

No answer.

"The Jura," he told them, "is a limestone formation. Limestone is developed from calcium deposits. Calcium deposits are the shells and bones and teeth of dead fish that have settled to the bottom of the sea."

They looked about them at the mountains and still wondered.

"All this means," he told them, "that we are walking on what was once the bottom of the sea. These fossil marine animals prove it."

This earth, he went on to explain, was millions of years old. Slowly, slowly, it went on changing. Once in past ages some mysterious force and pressure had caused the Jura to buckle upward. Much of Europe had once been sea bottom.

"Mother Nature has written her whole life story in the rocks. It is up to us to read it."

Louis Agassiz's teaching spread like a happy contagion. He began to give evening lectures for adults. Soon everyone—the farmers, the fishermen, the shopkeepers—knew they had only to begin a conversation with Louis Agassiz to receive a lesson in natural science.

Once more the fishermen in their small boats at the lake front smiled happily to see him coming. Only, now, he was tall, athletic and vigorous, a young man who never seemed to grow tired. Every time a strange fish came into their nets they would say,

"Save it for Professor Agassiz."

The leaders of the town, the well-to-do merchants, and men of the government, caught the fever, too. Science had come to Neuchâtel.

A Scientist of Two Worlds

"We must have a learned society here, a society for the study of natural sciences." Soon there came into existence The Society of Natural Sciences of Neuchâtel. Agassiz became its secretary, and it met at a private house in the evening to discuss scientific subjects.

"Ah, yes!" declared the optimistic Agassiz, "and you ought to have a Museum of Natural History as well."

The town fathers nodded and began to plan.

Through it all Agassiz was working on his two books, eager to complete them. But there is a limit to how much anyone can do. Cuvier had once warned Agassiz to be more prudent about his work. "Too much work kills," Cuvier had said. And the day soon came when Agassiz had to admit that Cuvier was right. He noticed that he was having trouble focusing his microscope. But wait! Was it the microscope? He looked about the room. The trouble proved to be with his own vision, the same blurriness he had experienced in Paris. Impulsively he rushed to a doctor.

"You must have a complete rest immediately or you may lose your eyesight altogether," the doctor told him.

For many weeks he had to be shut up in a darkened room—doing nothing. He wanted to finish his books! He wanted to be married! It was no use, though, and he knew it. He must stop and think of his health. He could not even write a letter to Cecile Braun.

"Is there any word from Cecile?" he would ask, and someone would read him her letter. "Is there any word from Dinkel?" Dinkel had remained in Paris to complete drawings he was making of fossils at the museums. "Yes, yes, Professor Agassiz. Dinkel reports that he is making great progress."

Gradually his eyes mended and he was permitted back to

work. He made a sensible change in his schedule. He decided to write only one book at a time, the one on fossil fishes, and he laid aside the work on fresh-water fishes.

Recovery meant that he and Cecile could go ahead with plans for their wedding, but her family had been watching Agassiz with growing doubts. He seemed too irresponsible about money, too wrapped up in his work, to make a good husband.

"Don't worry," Louis told Cecile. "There is to be a new museum here soon, and I think the town will buy my collection for it. Then we will have a handsome sum of money."

By the autumn of 1833, when he had been at Neuchâtel just about a year, he was able to journey to Karlsruhe—to renew his friendship with the Brauns and to marry Cecile.

"I hope I shall like it at Neuchâtel," she said. "Is it very different from Karlsruhe?"

"Oh, you will love it," he promised. "I have found an attractive little apartment for us there."

Cecile never really learned to like Neuchâtel. Her native tongue was German and she found French difficult. Neuchâtel seemed a very small town indeed after the fashionable city of Karlsruhe with its social life and interesting people.

But Louis and Cecile were really happy in the first years of their married life. They had faith in the future.

Cecile began to make some of the illustrations for his books on fishes, and Louis looked at her pictures with pride and said, "They are as fine as Dinkel's. Finer!" And they really were. Cecile had been studying with very good teachers and she had a great deal of talent.

Their faith was rewarded during their first few months together when Agassiz published Volume I of *Research on*

A Scientist of Two Worlds

Fossil Fishes. There were to be five volumes in all, and each volume of text was accompanied by its companion volume of illustrations. As other scientists began to read the text and examine Dinkel's drawings they knew that a great contribution was being made to both geology and zoology. "The work of a master," said more than one. Agassiz's method of classifying fossil fishes, chiefly according to their kinds of scales, made it possible to identify and understand more forms than ever before. His book gave scientists a whole new slant on all fishes. His work showed that the farther back in time a fish lived the more primitive was his structure. He showed by the scales, the skeletons, and the teeth as well, how fishes had developed through the ages from the most simple forms to the modern fishes.

His research with fish embryos revealed another startling fact. As the embryo of a modern fish developed, it passed through stages that resembled various ancient forms. In other words, if you watched a fish embryo through its growth, you would see the history of all fishes from ancient to modern.

In grouping and listing every fossil fish that he had been able to study in every possible museum, he showed to which period in the earth's history each belonged. He also gave the location where each fossil had been found.

He classified fossil fishes into four principal groups, according to their scales: Cycloids with round smooth scales, Ctenoids with scales that have small spines along one edge, Ganoids with scales shaped like a slanting rectangle or rhomboid, and Placoids whose scales were really like tiny, pointed teeth. The present-day shark has Placoid scales, and you may feel their sharp, prickly tips by rubbing your hand over the skin of a shark.

Neuchâtel

The Ganoids were the most important and largest group in Agassiz's classification. Some forms of Ganoids seem to have lived since the very earliest appearance of fishes on the earth. There are still some primitive descendents of the ancient Ganoids in the seas today. The garpike is one, and the sturgeon is another.

Present-day scientists no longer classify fishes on the basis of their scales alone. They feel that scales are only one of many important factors to be considered. In addition, during the last hundred years more and more types of fishes have been discovered.

About ninety per cent of the fishes in the world today are true "modern" fishes, that is, the most advanced in their development. Modern fishes have scales that overlap like the shingles of a roof and they have true bony skeletons. (The shark developed along different lines; he has the Placoid "tooth" scales and his skeleton is cartilage.) Modern fishes are generally called Teleosts, and they may have Cycloid, Ctenoid or Ganoid scales, but never Placoid.

Dinkel's illustrations were as valuable as Agassiz's text. Many of his enlarged drawings of one part or another of a fish were three-dimensional. Others showed exactly the impression an extinct fish had made upon a rock surface.

Louis's and Cecile's faith in the future was rewarded still further when three letters arrived that winter, one from Switzerland and the other two from England. All three were the result of publishing Volume I.

"Come visit me at my home in Bex," said the Swiss letter from Jean de Charpentier. "There are many interesting fossils in the rock and earth layers here in this part of the Alps."

Charpentier was the director of the salt mines near Bex,

A Scientist of Two Worlds

the engineer and scientist whom Agassiz had met when he was a student at Lausanne.

The first English letter was written by Dr. William Buckland, Professor of Geology at Exeter College, Oxford University. Dr. Buckland invited Agassiz to come to England and study the fossil fishes at Oxford Museum.

The second English letter was from Sir Charles Lyell, the world-famous geologist, who was Professor of Geology at Kings College, London.

Lyell was really the founder and creator of modern geology. He had recently completed publishing his famous work, *The Principles of Geology*. Lyell's *Principles* became the standard for geologists for generations to come. The earth was millions of years old, he said, and it had been changing slowly all through its history. It was still changing. The same forces that had always been at work were still at work. But changes took place so slowly that they were not noticeable in one lifetime, or even in several lifetimes. Where it is now cold the climate had once been tropical. The earth's appearance and the earth's climates kept changing. Rivers gradually wash land down into the sea; marine animals still die and their skeletons settle to the bottom, making calcium deposits; volcanoes still erupt, and earthquakes still happen; mountains are still growing; while somewhere else land is sinking into the sea; and the corals work diligently to build new islands and atolls.

Lyell was not the first to express this principle of slow and continuing change over millions of years. But he said it better than it had ever been said before, and he spent years collecting evidence. He traveled in Switzerland, France, England, Scotland, Italy, and everywhere he observed rocks and land formations and the fossils found in the different layers of the earth. At last he brought all his knowledge of geology together in one great work, just as Agassiz was doing with fossil fishes.

Dr. Lyell's letter to Agassiz said that the Geological Society of London had awarded Agassiz a prize of thirty-one pounds and ten shillings, to enable him to continue his work on fossil fishes. They knew that such a technical book would never be popular or profitable, but they felt it was so important they wanted to help him finish it. And Dr. Lyell added that the Society planned "to subscribe for it, and has already ordered a copy from the publishers." Professor Agassiz must not think that he was expected to send a complimentary copy.

Louis and his wife gazed at one another happily. He was rising rapidly in the world of science.

"And well you deserve to," said Cecile. "Now we must plan for your trip to England."

As a matter of fact, Agassiz made two trips to England, one in August 1834 and the other the next summer. How eagerly he was welcomed by learned men many years older than himself, this young man still in his twenties! Professors Buckland and Lyell especially took great delight in showing him around.

Agassiz was fascinated by the wonderful collection of fossils that he found in the museums in London, Oxford, Scotland, and Ireland. He must have every bit of information for his work; he must have pictures of every species of extinct fish.

"Leave Paris for a while," he wrote to Dinkel. "I want you to make drawings of all the important specimens here."

In England, Agassiz was able to study as many as two thousand specimens. Once again he left Dinkel behind to draw the pictures, and he returned to Neuchâtel to resume his teaching and writing.

A Scientist of Two Worlds

He found that the Society of Natural Science of Neuchâtel was waiting for him with great excitement after his first trip to England.

"You must give us a lecture on your findings in the British Isles," they insisted.

Of course, he did. He loved sharing knowledge. Not only did he give them a talk on the material in the British Museums, but during the winter he lectured frequently on other scientific subjects. One of his outstanding papers was on Echinoderms. The Echinoderms include starfishes, sea urchins, sea cucumbers, sea lilies, all animals with spiny skins and radial symmetry, that is, radiating out from the center like a star. Most animals have either radial symmetry or bilateral symmetry, with a right and left hand side. The very simplest forms are an exception.

Agassiz enjoyed hearing lectures by learned men as much as he enjoyed giving them. As far as he was concerned the most exciting and startling lecture of that winter of 1834-35 was delivered by Jean de Charpentier before a meeting of the Helvetic (Swiss) Society of Naturalists in the city of Lucerne. It wasn't about animal life at all, but about Swiss glaciers.

Around the Swiss countryside, said Charpentier, especially in the valleys, there are scattered great boulders that do not match the composition of the local mountains. That wasn't news. Anyone with half an eye who had ever been to Switzerland knew that. What startled Charpentier's audience was that he said he thought these boulders had been carried to their present location by glaciers.

Ridiculous! said most of the audience, including Agassiz, but the idea persisted in the back of Agassiz's mind. He returned to his work on fossil fishes, his classes of eager young students, his field trips. Only now, when he came upon a boulder beside the road, he looked at it wonderingly.

Letters of praise still continued to come to him from different parts of the world. In the spring one came from Yale College in America. Yale was subscribing to his volumes of fossil fishes. "A great work," the letter called it. Yale was passing the word along to Harvard College, to the Boston libraries, and to the Boston Natural History Society.

America! Agassiz thought. How very far away it was. There must be thousands of fossil specimens buried in the rock layers of the American continent. And how many strange and new living plants and animals must there be? He remembered how many new fishes Martius and Spix had found in the Amazon River alone.

Suddenly his work on fossil fishes struck a snag, a serious snag. His publisher Cotta in Stuttgart announced that the project was too expensive, it was to be discontinued. Mr. Cotta himself had died nearly three years earlier, and those who were running his company did not feel his personal regard for Agassiz's work.

Maybe Cotta could give up the project, but Agassiz could not. The idea of not finishing his work simply did not occur to him. He had received a second cash award in England, from the British Association, for his fossil fishes. The town of Neuchâtel had purchased his specimens for its new Natural History Museum, and the price had been generous. Part of the sum had come from the King of Prussia. His list of subscribers was growing.

"I shall publish them myself," said Louis Agassiz.

His wife just shut her eyes. She knew there would be no money for anything else until the last volume had come out. She was expecting a child, that would not only increase their expenses but would allow her less time for his drawings.

But Louis Agassiz was Louis Agassiz. He was a scientist devoted to his work. He was not a financier, and he never would be.

"I must find a top-notch lithographer," he mused. "Top-notch."

The child they were expecting was born December 17, 1835, and was named Alexander. Agassiz was beside himself with joy.

"A son!" he declared. "He will be a scientist!"

"We cannot be sure of that," Cecile warned him. "Better wait and see."

"With so many scientists in your family and mine, he cannot fail," said Agassiz with a gay sweep of his arm.

5

AGASSIZ'S ICE AGE

HIS new son, his extra labors in doing his own publishing, his teaching, his lectures at the town's learned society—all of his activities could not make him forget what Charpentier had said about glaciers. He spoke of it often.

"Don't forget Charpentier's invitation to spend a vacation with him," said Cecile.

Agassiz hadn't forgotten, but his last two summers had been spent in the British Isles.

"I feel a deep admiration for Charpentier. I do not know why he has taken such a foolish stand with regard to glaciers."

"Perhaps a visit would clear up the matter. Remember he also said that there are many fossils in that part of the Alps," Cecile suggested.

The exchange of a few letters settled the matter. As soon as the school term was ended, Louis and Cecile Agassiz and six-months-old Alexander traveled to Bex, not far beyond

A Scientist of Two Worlds

Lausanne in southern Switzerland. Bex was a pretty village in the Rhone Valley with tall mountains in the background. The Charpentiers—Mr. and Mrs. Jean de Charpentier and their seven-year-old daughter—had a home just outside of town, and the Agassiz's rented a cottage near them.

Charpentier was still director of the salt mines near Bex, but he spent every spare minute with Louis Agassiz. He was overjoyed to discover Agassiz's new interest in glaciers.

"I must show you every piece of evidence that I have found of the work of glaciers," he insisted. "I must convince you that my theory about the boulders is correct."

Together they hiked and climbed over the countryside in the daytime. Charpentier showed Agassiz flat rock surfaces that were marked by lines and scratches where a glacier had once traveled over them. He showed him deposits of gravel that had been dropped by a glacier as it melted and retreated.

"There was once a glacier," said Charpentier, "that spread all down through the Rhone Valley, sculpturing and marking the landscape. And when it receded it left behind it boulders and gravel along the way."

Agassiz saw so much evidence of this very thing with his own eyes while he was with Charpentier that he had to change his mind.

In the evenings the two men talked ice and glaciers. How did glaciers form? What caused one to come flowing down through a valley and then withdraw? How could solid ice flow? They were talking more than a hundred years ago, and at that time most of their questions remained to be answered.

Now we know that a glacier results from snow accumulating in a cold place year after year without melting away. As the snow grows deeper and heavier it becomes packed and solidified into an icy mass, and begins to spread

62

Agassiz's Ice Age

like molasses on a plate. There are glaciers today in the regions of permanent snow, in the Alps, the Himalayas, the Andes, at the north and south poles. A glacier in a flat region like Greenland will spread until it reaches the sea and then pieces will break off and float around, making icebergs. In high mountainous regions glaciers find their way down valleys and behave like slow, creeping rivers of ice. When they reach warm altitudes, especially during the summer months, they melt and feed the mountain streams.

Agassiz and Charpentier reviewed together every scrap of information they had about glaciers.

Scheuchzer had been the first important glacialist. He had thought of glaciers as moving. Then came de Saussure. No one made more observations than he—all over Switzerland— Mont Blanc, Mont Rose, the Bernese Alps. He even measured the depths of glaciers. The Glacier des Bois, he said, was a hundred feet thick. Then came Hugi, the great geologist. He spent years studying glaciers, and he had a station in the Aar Valley, right on top of the glacier.

"It was Venetz who started me thinking," said Charpentier. "He wrote a paper that almost no one knows about. In it he said that this whole valley of the Rhone River was once occupied by a glacier, and I went out to see for myself."

"And then I came to see for myself," said Agassiz, "and here we are."

To make the summer even more interesting, Dr. I. Venetz, who was also an engineer in the same region of Switzerland, stopped at Bex for a visit while Agassiz was there. And to make Agassiz's summer really complete, Karl Schimper came to Bex as well and joined the group for a while. Agassiz had not seen him for five years, and they had a great deal to talk over.

63

A Scientist of Two Worlds

That winter found Louis Agassiz excitedly and vigorously examining the Jura around Neuchâtel for telltale signs of former glaciers. And he found plenty! Rocks striped with scratches, deposits of gravel, and in the valleys scattered granite boulders from the Alps that did not match the sedimentary rocks of the Jura.

Agassiz could scarcely contain himself. His fevered imagination struggled to grasp the meaning of all this evidence. Former glaciers! Glaciers that had retreated before the warm temperatures! What did it mean? At last his vision and genius broke through to a great truth. There had been vast glaciers! Not just in Switzerland, but all over the world, and all at the same time! An ice age! The world and everything that lived upon it must have lived through an age of ice and snow.

He knew that all the facts of nature were related. He had been studying and hunting fossil fishes for a long time. He knew that they were found in the different layers of the earth's crust. He knew that the deeper down the layer in which he found a fossil, the older must be both layer and fossil. He knew, therefore, that the history of the earth and the history of life on the earth were related. Whatever happened to the earth, happened to all the plants and creatures on the earth. Had some of these fossils died off in a deep freeze? Was that why they were extinct? As a young student he had seen at the Museum of Stuttgart the bones of a great mammoth, an extinct mammoth, found sixty feet deep in ice in Siberia.

The whole thing was so clear to Agassiz that he had to stop and remember that his idea was only a theory. But the Ice Age was a good theory! It was by new theories that science moved ahead. They pointed the way.

Agassiz's Ice Age

In England a scientist named John Dalton was talking and writing about an atomic theory. All elements, said Dalton, were composed of minute particles called atoms. Who could tell where that would lead to? Scientists must listen to one another's theories.

The summer after Agassiz's visit to Bex, the Helvetic Society of Natural Sciences held its meeting at Neuchâtel. Louis Agassiz was president of the Society at that time, and he stood on the platform to preside as eminent scientists from all over the world filtered into the hall. The place was soon packed.

"Will Agassiz lecture this year?" they said to one another.

"Oh, yes indeed!"

"Splendid! I've never known a scientist who understands as much about fishes as he."

A flurry of happy excitement spread over the audience as Agassiz stepped forward, papers in hand. No one could make science live the way he did. His science sounded like adventure fiction.

"Gentlemen, very dear friends and associates," Agassiz began, and he told them how happy Neuchâtel was to be host to so many eminent scientists. "We all welcome research which is the tie that unites all the sciences which interest our society." He went on to generalize about the work of the astronomer, the chemist, the physicist, the natural historian, the geologist. They were all striving toward the same goal.

In another few minutes his audience began to grow tense. Dr. Agassiz was not going to talk about fishes as they had calmly supposed. What was he saying?

"Quite recently, two of our colleagues provoked heated discussions with their research. The nature of the land where

65

A Scientist of Two Worlds

we are meeting induces me to present to you a new subject which, I think, is supported by evidence in the slopes of our Jura range. I wish to speak of glaciers, of moraines, and of erratic blocks."

Dead silence!

By erratic blocks he meant, of course, the granite boulders scattered around in the valley in which they were meeting, blocks that did not match the Jura but did match the distant Alps. He told his audience of the observations made by Venetz, Charpentier, and himself. He described all the evidence he himself had seen to indicate that there had once been a great glacier that spread all down through the Rhone Valley, and evidence of another glacier covering the valley in which they were now meeting. He described the polished surfaces of the rocks, the deposits of gravel, the boulders. He reminded them of the close relationship between biology and geology, between life on the earth and the history of the earth. Then—while they seemed to stop breathing altogether—he presented his new theory: The Ice Age.

"A Siberian winter was established for a time upon the earth covering its rich vegetation and big animal life. There are a few of these huge mammals in the warm regions of India and Africa today. Death enveloped all nature in a shroud, and the cold was so intense that the ice grew hard and massive."

It was his theory, he told his shocked listeners, that a great ice sheet formed at the North Pole and spread as far as the Mediterranean and Caspian seas and down over the plains of North America. The same occurred at the South Pole.

Agassiz's Ice Age is no longer a theory; it is a known fact. He was mistaken about the location of the ice sheets, and they did not extend as far as he thought. In North America there

66

Agassiz's Ice Age

were two principal glaciers during the Ice Age: one in Labrador that extended westward as far as the base of the Canadian Rockies and southward as far as New Jersey, Pennsylvania, the Ohio River and Missouri River; and a smaller one that was concentrated mainly in the Canadian Rockies. There were smaller glaciers farther south in the Rockies and on Greenland. In Europe the principal glaciers spread down from the Alps and from Scandinavia. In Asia they formed in the Himalayas and in Siberia. But they did not cover the whole hemisphere.

The fact that Agassiz was mistaken about some of his details is not really important. The important thing is that Agassiz gave scientists a new idea, the idea that there had once been an Ice Age. They could take up his idea all over the world and search for more and more evidence to refine and improve it. This they eventually did, after Agassiz had started them off.

Geologists have since discovered that the earth had four ice ages with warm periods in between. The first ice age occurred about 750,000 years ago, and the fourth brings us up to date, because it isn't finished. There are still ice caps in the Arctic and Antarctic regions and mountain glaciers in the Alps, the Himalayas, the Andes and the Rockies. Is the earth growing gradually warm again? It would seem at times that the climate around us is becoming milder. What will happen when all the ice caps and glaciers have disappeared once more? What will become of the sturdy fur-bearing animals of the far north? That region was warm in the ancient past. And if the glaciers disappear from the Alps, will the Rhone River also disappear? It starts in the melting ice of a glacier. Will other rivers like the Rhine and Danube shrink? They are fed principally by streams of glacial water.

A Scientist of Two Worlds

That day at Neuchâtel, when Agassiz concluded his talk and sat down, his audience was stunned. Then, like a sud denly rising wind, a murmur of indignation swept the room. Dr. Leopold de Buch, one of the most outstanding geologists of the day, stood bolt upright and raised his arms in the air.

"Show us the proof!" he shouted to Agassiz, and his voice boomed through the room. "Show us the proof!" With that de Buch stalked out of the hall in an angry huff.

Agassiz remained outwardly calm and serene, but during the rest of the sessions of the Helvetic Society and afterward his mind was disturbed by de Buch's challenge. De Buch had asked for proof, and de Buch was right. A man cannot be a true scientist unless he is completely honest, and Agassiz was a true scientist. De Buch, the whole Helvetic Society, scientists everywhere, were entitled to proof. Otherwise, he had no right to expect them to believe in his Ice Age.

De Buch was not the only one to take Agassiz to task. He received a long, anxious letter from his beloved Dr. Humboldt:

"For mercy's sake, take care of your health which is so dear to us. I am afraid you work too much, and that you spread your intellect over too many subjects at once. I think that you should concentrate your moral and also your pecuniary strength upon this beautiful work on fossil fishes. In so doing you will render a greater service to positive geology, than by these general considerations (a little icy withall). . . . Your ice frightens me. . . ."

Agassiz had no intention of taking time away from his fossil fishes. Glaciers were his vacation project. Next summer he was going back into the Alps and find the proof that de Buch demanded. Maybe some day he would go farther than the Alps. Perhaps he would be able to go to other parts of the earth seeking proof of his Ice Age.

Meanwhile, he was making arrangements to publish his work on fossil fishes. Hercule Nicolet, a lithographer living in the same Canton of Neuchâtel, came to the town of Neuchâtel to help Agassiz establish a company. They found a building not far from town, and before very long Agassiz had a whole staff working for him, among them Dinkel and one other artist. The whole thing was rather badly managed, because Agassiz had no business ability and neither did Nicolet. Inefficiency made it more expensive.

But somehow Agassiz got everything done.

A second child, a daughter, named Ida, was born to him and Cecile on August 8, 1837, and Louis Agassiz sat happily by his wife's bedside chatting about the future. Alexander was a year and eight months old, running about, mischievous and merry.

"By the time they are old enough to go to school my volumes on fossil fishes will be completed and there will be more money for all of us," Agassiz promised his wife.

Cecile just looked at him and did not answer. There were times when she grew a little discouraged over the penny-pinching that she had to do, even though she did understand the importance of her husband's work. She knew there would never be any cash profit from it. She only hoped he could manage to complete it without going too deeply into debt, but she wasn't at all sure that he could.

A few weeks after Ida was born, Louis Agassiz engaged Edouard Desor to be his personal secretary. He couldn't afford a secretary any more than he could afford to be his own publisher. He could imagine an Ice Age or the exact appearance of an extinct fish, but he could not comprehend the value or limits of money.

A Scientist of Two Worlds

"You can have a room in my house and take your meals with me and my wife," Agassiz told Desor. "That will be part of your pay."

Desor was a poverty-stricken law student at the time, and so he was glad to accept the little bit that Agassiz could pay.

"He knows nothing of natural science, or any kind of science for that matter," Cecile said to Louis. "Are you sure Desor is a wise choice?"

"He is very intelligent," said Agassiz, "and very good at translating into French and German. He can take care of my correspondence and keep the accounts for my publishing projects."

Louis Agassiz remained hard at work all winter at Neuchâtel. He had long since forgotten that his health could give him any trouble, and indeed it seemed that he had the capacity of ten men. The fact that he had so many irons in the fire did not hurt any one job that he was doing, because, while he was on a task, he gave it his full attention and forgot everything else. When he walked into the classroom to teach, or took his young students on a field trip, he gave his young charges his whole self. As they gathered round him, watching him turn a leaf or a rock over in the palm of his hand, they felt that Agassiz belonged to them, only to them. He cared about nothing else in the world. When he sat down with his secretary, Edouard Desor, he gave *him* his whole self. He worked on his fossil fishes the same way.

Desor soon caught the natural science fever and began to study. After a couple of years with Agassiz, Desor had absorbed enough scientific knowledge to assist Agassiz in some of his research.

The only thing that took Agassiz away from his work that winter season was the death of his father in the early fall. He

Agassiz's Ice Age

returned to Concise for a few weeks to help his mother settle matters. Since the house his parents had lived in was the parsonage, Mrs. Agassiz could not remain there. She decided to live with each of her four children in turn.

Toward spring Agassiz began to make plans for an extraordinary summer, his expedition into the Alps. As he mulled over his Alpine adventure he thought of Arnold Guyot, his boyhood friend, the Neuchâtel scientist who had been part of the happy group at Cecile's home in Karlsruhe. Guyot was in Paris, and Agassiz journeyed to Paris to pay him a visit. They spent hours together, talking about glaciers. Agassiz explained his Ice Age theory, and Guyot listened with some doubts.

"I was very doubtful myself," said Agassiz, "until I investigated. Why do you not go to the Alps this summer as I am doing? I am going to the Bernese Oberland. Perhaps you could go to the central Alps. We can compare our findings."

At last Guyot consented.

"Very well," he said. "I shall see you here in Paris next autumn."

Agassiz went home in high spirits to organize his expedition to the Alps in the Canton of Berne. His new secretary, Desor, would go with him, and so would Dinkel and his brother-in-law Max Braun, as well as two of his young students.

"We are going high up into the Alps," he told them, "into the regions of permanent snows, as far as the Rosenlaui Glacier."

6

A HOTEL ON
A GLACIER

AGASSIZ'S first scientific caravan set out from Neuchâtel the beginning of August, 1838. The six men headed southeastward toward the heart of the Swiss Alps. While the roads were fair, they traveled in coaches, but soon the passes grew narrow and the paths wound along steep ledges, and they had to change to muleback or hike along on foot.

Agassiz had never visited this part of Switzerland before, and he strode along with great zest, reveling in the scenery and in every scientific discovery that he made.

"See here!" he would call to his companions, showing them a rock polished smooth by a former glacier.

He would walk across a wide flat rock surface striped with deep grooves, or strike a pile of glacial gravel with the toe of his boot.

"Now look at this!" he said another time, holding a rock

A Hotel on a Glacier

in his hand, breaking it apart with his geologist's hammer, and looking at it with a magnifying glass. "This rock came from somewhere else. It didn't walk by itself, and it is too far from home for small boys to have thrown it."

They were following, more or less, the Aar River upstream toward its mother glacier. Each little Swiss hamlet or village or town that they passed through seemed to cluster in a valley, often on the shore of a lake, shut in by towering, snow-capped mountains. The valleys themselves were green and fertile with grazing cattle and vineyards.

By the time the party reached the town of Meiringen, the men had their notebooks full of notes and Dinkel's sketchbook was full of sketches. The climb up to Meiringen had been steep and strenuous, but they were going still higher. They could expect the journey to grow more and more rugged. As long as there were towns along the way they could stop at inns for meals and lodgings, but they would soon leave these comforts behind them.

"Now we are really in the Bernese Oberland," said Agassiz.

Down beneath them the Aar River flowed quietly through its valley. Its water was porcelain blue. They continued on up the Aar as far as a pass through the mountains called the Grimsel Pass. There the Aar was no longer quiet. It rushed swiftly down a steep narrow bed.

Now and again the travelers saw a herd of chamois, timid, alert, one standing guard while the others grazed.

"Look," said Agassiz, pointing to a plant. "Here is the lichen upon which the chamois feed. At these heights nothing but mosses and lichens will grow."

He gazed about him at the mountains and the Grimsel Pass through them. Beyond the pass was the source of the the River Aar, the Aar Glacier. He knew he must come back and examine the glacier, even though it wasn't possible on this trip. Their goal this time was the Rosenlaui Glacier.

"Ah!" sighed Agassiz. "How many summers will I need?"

The party turned back northward to Meiringen, and from there after a rest they climbed into the mountains, higher and higher, only stopping now and again to catch their breath. Far below them the green side of the mountain sloped far away, dotted by little villages, above them the snow and ice of the Rosenlaui Glacier spread out among the rocks and passes. They climbed on up to the glacier, examining its edge, the pile of gravel it was pushing along in front of itself. They walked on top of the glacier to examine its ice and the stones and pebbles imbedded in it.

Far in the distance they could see the famous snow-covered group of peaks called the Wetterhorn.

When they had finished examining the glacier they descended gradually along the sloping side of the mountain until they reached the village of Grindelwald. There they sank into chairs around an inn table, tired but happy. Their strength came back quickly as they ate their luncheon. They were young men, and they all loved mountain climbing. The Alpine air had given them a great appetite and filled them with zest, and their voices boomed with happy laughter.

At a nearby table a tourist perked up his ears as he heard one of the young men called "Agassiz."

"Can that young man be related to the famous Professor Agassiz?" he asked.

"That young man *is* the famous Professor Agassiz," he was told.

Agassiz was gazing around him at the scenery, completely unaware that he was attracting attention. Grindelwald was in a fertile green valley surrounded by lofty mountains

A Hotel on a Glacier

covered with thick pine forests. Above the pine forests arose the glistening white peaks of Jungfrau, Finsteraarhorn, Faulhorn, the Wetterhorn, and Schreckhorn.

The six scientists were back in Neuchâtel on August 24. What a short trip! Agassiz thought. Just enough to whet his appetite for more.

"You know," he mused aloud, "the summer is not yet ended. There is time to see another glacier."

In an amazingly short time he had organized another caravan, a larger one, and was on his way toward another chain of the Alps in southern Switzerland and France, the group that includes Mont Blanc, the highest peak of the Alps.

"Mont Blanc has several glaciers," Agassiz told his companions, "and the biggest is called the Mer de Glace (sea of ice)."

Their route took them due south, through Bex, where Agassiz intended to stop and see Charpentier. There Agassiz tried to persuade his friend to join the group, but Charpentier could not leave his work just then.

Agassiz and his companions went on southward, following the Rhone Valley for a while. This was the region where Charpentier had found so many evidences of an ancient glacier, and as the coach rolled along the hard road that ran beside the river Agassiz stopped often to examine the terrain.

The Rhone changes its direction at Martigny, and there the travelers left it and went on southward, through the mountain pass known as Col de Balme. The road from Col de Balme sloped gradually down into the Chamonix Valley, and the village of Chamonix was their next stopping place.

"Wait until you see Mont Blanc by moonlight," they were told. "Here in this valley, even though we are three thousand feet above sea level, we are so shut in by tall mountains that the moon seldom finds us at all. But she will light up the white tip of the peak."

Mother Nature gave them their spectacle that night, and next morning they started their trek up the mountain. The path became more rugged and dangerous with each step they took, and they had to pay careful attention to their experienced guides. Each hiker carried a stout walking stick as tall as himself with a sharp spike on its tip.

When they were almost upon the Mer de Glace, their rocky path went up over a rise of ground and down a slight incline and there they were—looking at something they could never have imagined. It was indeed a sea, nearly a mile wide, caught in an icy spell. A traveler once wrote that the Mer de Glace looked like a "lake, wrought into tumult and fury by whirlwinds, and then instantaneously frozen." Its surface was dangerously rough, with ice piled high in some places and split open in crevasses in others. Some of the ice had formed into glistening crystals that gleamed with all the colors of the rainbow; the level places were a blue-green sea color.

"If you wish to walk out on the glacier," said Agassiz, "stay behind your guide."

"Could the whole world once have looked like this?" asked one of his companions.

"It could, indeed," Agassiz replied.

Then, as he stood at the edge of the Mer de Glace, he gave them a careful lecture on glaciers.

Like the first excursion, this second was over too quickly for Agassiz. All winter he promised himself that next summer he would really make a careful examination of a Swiss glacier. He wanted to live with one for a long time, study its behavior, its structure, learn its whole story. Every glacier, he was discovering, had its own personality; every glacier taught him something different.

In September he went to Porrentruy in northern Switzerland to attend a meeting of the Geological Society of France. Of course, there was a lively discussion on glaciers, and Agassiz, Charpentier, Arnold Guyot, and others were on their feet from time to time in the big gathering, defending their ideas. Louis Agassiz presented a paper that he had just written called, "Observations on Glaciers." Bit by bit he was presenting to the scientific world the proof that de Buch had demanded.

His *Fossil Fishes* showed great progress during the winter. As each new volume of the work was completed and sent out to the list of subscribers, Agassiz's fame and prestige increased. Scientists read the text and looked at the accurate pictures.

"This is Agassiz at his best," one after another said. "I hope he gets over his moonshine about glaciers soon."

If anyone had asked Cecile Agassiz, she would probably have said that his publishing was the moonshine she wished he'd get over. Desor was living right in the house, and he was becoming a vain, difficult man, currying Agassiz's favor to prevent others from receiving too much of it. He gradually built up strained relations with a young doctor named Karl Vogt who was working with Agassiz and taking his meals with the family.

In order to keep his lithographic plant busy Agassiz had begun publishing the works of others. The books he decided to publish didn't sell well, and he was in more of a financial hole than ever. But he just could not get depressed over money matters when there was so much scientific data to be

A Scientist of Two Worlds

gathered. Come spring he was in a high good humor over his next trip into the Alps.

The party starting out from Neuchâtel on August 9, 1839, was made up chiefly of scientists: Agassiz, Desor, and six others. Agassiz took his companions as far south as Zermatt. From there they examined glaciers coming down from the two famous mountain peaks, Mont Rose and the Matterhorn. After that they journeyed up the Rhone River Valley to the source of the Rhone.

By the time they reached the pass in the Alps called the Furka, the Rhone had become a swift stream hurrying down the steep descents, and when they had climbed higher they reached its glacier. The Rhone River gushed from a cave at the base of the glacier.

"Here is the origin of an important river," Agassiz said, "the melting of ice and snow of a glacier. All along the line it is fed by other glacial streams. The Aar River also begins in a glacier."

They were not far from the Grimsel, since the Aar River rises in the same general region as the Rhone. Once more they descended into the Rhone Valley and headed for the Grimsel Pass.

"The Aar Glacier is the one that Professor Hugi examined so carefully," Agassiz reminded his companions as they rested at an inn.

Soon they were toiling up the steep and rocky road to the Grimsel Pass, and only reached it after three hours. On the other side they descended into a shallow valley and soon came upon a solitary, rather primitive farmhouse. This was the Grimsel Hospice, or lodging place for mountain climbers. A man and his wife lived there, keeping goats and making cheese for market, growing a few vegetables in their garden.

A Hotel on a Glacier

They were shut off from the world by heavy snows during the long winter, and they welcomed summer visitors.

"We wish to make this our headquarters while we explore the Aar Glacier," Agassiz explained to the landlord.

The party of explorers all slept in the one spare room, the sitting room, along with five or six farm hands, and the landlord and his wife occupied a small bedroom.

Early next morning they set out with guides recommended by the landlord. On up the Aar Valley they went until they reached the edge of the glacier, and from there on they walked on top of the glacier, still going upstream. If they continued far enough the glacier would divide into two branches.

Agassiz and his friends walked along the glacier for about three hours, and when they had almost reached the point where it divides into two paths, they saw ahead of them an enormous block of granite. The boulder was perched right on top of the glacier and had probably rolled down onto it from above. If glaciers really moved, then that boulder was taking a quiet ride down the Aar Valley.

Near the boulder was a crude cabin, and one of the guides declared that it was the cabin that Professor Hugi had built.

"So!" cried Agassiz.

It is a scientist's duty to doubt everything until it has been proved. After all, this might be just a legend. So they hurried to the cabin and looked inside. There was hay on the floor that Hugi might have slept on.

"Here!" shouted one of the men excitedly, picking up a bottle.

Inside of the bottle were some papers, and the men crowded around as one of them spread out two letters and read their contents.

"They were written by Hugi! This *was* his cabin!"

79

A Scientist of Two Worlds

"What did Hugi write?"

"Here! He first built this cabin in 1827. That is twelve years ago. When he returned in 1830, three years later, he found the cabin had moved several hundred feet from its original location. This proves that glaciers flow."

"What about the second letter?"

"The second letter was written in 1836. After nine years he found that the cabin had moved more than two thousand feet from its original position."

Agassiz gazed at Hugi's letters with deep satisfaction, and he looked a long time at the cabin that had been riding along on the glacier.

"I am coming back," he announced. "I am coming back here next year and build a cabin of my own and make the same and many more observations."

That winter in Neuchâtel Agassiz added one more task to his teaching-writing-publishing-editing-researching program. He began to write a book on glaciers, called *Studies on Glaciers*. With it was to be a companion volume, an atlas of thirty-two pictures of glaciers.

When four-year-old Alexander Agassiz ran to his father, Agassiz would hold him high in the air and declare, "You are a Swiss! You must learn to climb mountains very soon. You must learn to love the Alps!"

"He is still a baby!" the boy's mother would protest.

"Nonsense!" said the boy's father. "Soon he will be scaling mountain peaks by himself."

Agassiz was making definite plans for his station on the Aar Glacier, and he chose his companions very carefully for the second trip. Desor and Karl Vogt were going, and one other scientist, and two of Agassiz's students. One of the

A Hotel on a Glacier

students was François de Pourtalès.

The caravan that finally set out for the Aar Glacier in the spring was loaded with scientific gear: barometers, thermometers, hygrometers, psychrometers, and drilling apparatus. Agassiz was determined to learn the whole personality of the Aar Glacier.

Again they made the Grimsel Hospice their base of operations, and started from there early in the morning with two guides. When they finally reached Hugi's cabin, they stared in amazement. The powerful driving force of the glacier had demolished it. After examining the scattered pieces, they went a little distance until they found a huge rock against an embankment. Tilted over the rock was another flat rock that formed a kind of roof.

"Here is the beginning of our station," they decided. With two walls and a roof already prepared, they needed only to build another wall and hang a blanket across the entrance. They stored their provisions in a nearby cave.

"A first class hotel!" said one, as they rolled up in their blankets for the night.

"We shall call it the Hôtel des Neuchâtelois," said another, meaning, Hotel of the Men from Neuchâtel.

For the next eight days they worked constantly at their observations. They rose each morning about four o'clock, since the guides who returned to the Grimsel Hospice each night usually appeared by then. Once up, they lighted the fire, made hot chocolate, and washed in ice water. Then they went out into the bitter cold air to read their instruments.

Agassiz watched the thermometers, hygrometers, psychrometer and barometer himself with the help of Pourtalès. Since Vogt was a naturalist Agassiz appointed him to investigate the "red snow" and other plant life in and about the glacier.

"The redness of the snow at times is due to microscopic organisms," Vogt had said.

Another studied the types of rocks. Desor observed the atmosphere and the moraines with the help of the other student.

"Will we go higher up?" one of the young men asked eagerly. "Perhaps to the Finsteraarhorn?" Then he added, "Or the Jungfrau?"

Agassiz nodded. "In a few days," he promised, "we shall start to explore the region. Now come here and help me drill holes in the glacier. I want to take its temperature at different depths."

Another time he said, "Help me drive these stakes."

The boys helped eagerly without understanding as Agassiz drove stakes deeply into the ice. The stakes formed a straight row across the glacier.

"I suspect," he explained, "that different parts of the glacier travel at different rates of speed. Next summer I shall return to examine the stakes. If they are still in a straight line, which I do not expect, then I shall know I was wrong."

The days flew by, because they were all so engrossed in their work. Much to their surprise one late morning, they looked up from their instruments to see a group of mountain climbers struggling and toiling up the glacier toward them. Occasionally travelers who liked mountain-climbing, came as far as the Grimsel Hospice, but no visitors were expected as far up as the Hôtel des Neuchâtelois.

"Women!" declared one of the scientists.

Agassiz needed only one glance to recognize his wife, and he loped down the icy grade to greet her. Yes, there she was, smiling and pleased, accompanied by her sister Emmy Braun

A Hotel on a Glacier

and an Alpine guide. To Agassiz's utter joy he saw his son Alexander sitting in a basket strapped to the guide's back. Tenderly he lifted the boy out and stood him on the glacier.

"He is a high-spirited little fellow," said the guide, "and very brave."

They had a gay dinner party that day, much better than the usual bread and cheese and mutton, for Cecile and Emmy had brought fresh food with them.

The visitors returned to the Hospice before dark, and the scientists returned to their work in better spirits than ever.

When Agassiz finally walked into the house the end of August, Cecile could see by his triumphant air that he had brought home volumes of proof for his Ice Age.

Before he settled down, he made a trip to the British Isles. There he spoke at a meeting of scientists in Glasgow, and he found them very reluctant to accept his ideas on glaciers. While he was in Scotland he went on some field trips among the mountains and found many signs of an Ice Age. He then read a paper on glaciers to the Geological Society of London, "On Glaciers and the Evidence of their Having Once Existed in Scotland, Ireland and England." He found London scientists more open-minded, and managed to convert Buckland and Lyell to his theory.

Back to Neuchâtel he went, happier than ever, to put the finishing touches on his *Studies on Glaciers.* Before the year was out it was a published book.

He and Desor made a short visit to the Aar and Rosenlaui glaciers in March, still the dead of winter in the Alps. They found their hotel completely buried under snow. Agassiz wanted to see whether there was any water given off by melting ice in the winter time. He decided that the only water that came from glaciers in the winter was ground water.

83

A Scientist of Two Worlds

By the time he and Desor reached their inn they realized what a foolish thing they had done to visit glaciers in the winter. Their faces were purple and their eyes puffy and painful. Agassiz's lower lip was badly swollen.

His friend Arnold Guyot went with him to the Aar during the summer of 1841, along with Vogt, Desor, and several others. Triumphantly Agassiz showed them his row of stakes. They stood in a curved line, the stakes in the center of the glacier having traveled farther than those near the edge.

The men remained a whole month, and the high point of their stay was the incident in which Agassiz almost became part of a glacier himself. They were busily boring a big hole in the glacier, trying to measure its thickness, when suddenly the boring rod broke through into a hollow place.

"How far down are you?" asked Agassiz.

"One hundred twenty feet, Professor."

If there was a cave inside of the glacier he must know all about it. He moved about with great animation while instruments were lowered into the cave. They didn't tell him what he wanted to know. He must go down into that cave himself.

Placing a strong tripod over the hole, he seated himself on a board on ropes and instructed his friends to let him down slowly. Glaciers, he knew from his observations, were formed in layers, season after season. Here was a chance to observe the layers or bands on the inside. Down, down, down he descended into the ice for eighty feet. He soon discovered that the inside was all divided into hollows and tunnels which were formed as the water from the melting ice worked its way down through these chambers, until it found its way out at the base and flowed down the mountain.

A Hotel on a Glacier

He maneuvered around on his suspended chair into one chamber large enough to accommodate him. The ropes let him farther down, and suddenly his feet were in ice cold water. Agassiz shouted up that he wanted to be hauled out. His assistants misunderstood him and lowered him deeper into the bitter cold water. The plunge almost took his breath away, but he managed to shout again, and the second time they understood him.

As they slowly hauled him up out of the hole, he looked upward. Giant stalactites of ice hung above him. If one were jarred loose by the rope it could crash down on his head and kill him. Carefully he guided the ropes of his chair until he was once more on the surface. His friends stripped his wet clothes off of him at once.

"If I had known all the danger down there," said Agassiz, as a guide rubbed him briskly with a towel, "I should not have gone down."

"I am glad to hear that," said Guyot.

"Don't anyone follow my example," he ordered.

"Don't worry, Professor!" they all promised him.

Agassiz used his Hôtel des Neuchâtelois for three summers and then built a stronger and more comfortable cabin which he called the Hotel of the Arch. The following summer he abandoned it and built a third called The Pavilion.

Louis Agassiz returned to the Aar Glacier each summer for five years, taking important scientists with him on each trip, key men from such places as Edinburgh and Cambridge.

He made his last trip to the Aar in 1845, and then another scientist agreed to take over his observations. Shortly afterward, Agassiz completed his second book on glaciers, *The Glacial System*.

7

A GREAT WORK
COMPLETED

AFTER the exercise in the mountains in the summertime, Agassiz always returned to his desk and his classroom glowing with good humor and energy; and his good humor spread to everyone around him. His own children in particular romped about him happily. There was a third child, a daughter named Pauline, who had been born in February 1841, and Ida was growing fast. Alexander in particular was becoming more spirited every day.

Cecile's excitement was apt to wear off first. She was doing her best to run a household on what her husband earned minus what he spent on his adventures. There were times when help had to come from her relatives or his.

"I am becoming discouraged, Louis," she said more than once.

Louis Agassiz was so engrossed in science that he did not seem to realize how serious his household problems were,

A Great Work Completed

or that his wife was not a robust person. When a letter came from the King of Prussia, enclosing a gift of nearly two hundred pounds for his work on glaciers, he waved the check in the air and declared,

"Ah, you see? The King wishes me to continue my work on glaciers."

It did distress Agassiz that his beloved teacher, Humboldt, was still not convinced about his Ice Age theory. But on the other hand he heard that the English scientist, Charles Darwin, was following his work on glaciers and beginning to agree with him. Darwin was even out examining the Welsh Mountains himself.

"The valley about me here," Darwin wrote from North Wales to a colleague, "and the site of the inn at which I am now writing must once have been covered by at least 800 or 1,000 feet in thickness of solid ice.... These glaciers have been grand agencies."

The letter found its way eventually into Agassiz's hands.

Darwin was about the same age as Agassiz, and he had spent his childhood and youth in Shrewsbury in western England, near the border of Wales. His father had been a doctor, and so it was natural that he should study medicine. But he was another young man who discovered that he preferred natural science. When he was only twenty-two he was selected to be the naturalist aboard the H. M. S. *Beagle*. The *Beagle* spent five years touring about the world, charting coasts and harbors for the British Admiralty. On that trip Darwin collected volumes of information about plants and animals in the Canary Islands, the Cape Verde Islands, the coast of Brazil, Argentina, and Chile, and many islands in the Pacific. He had returned from his trip and was Secretary of the Geological Society of London the autumn that Agassiz

A Scientist of Two Worlds

addressed that group "On Glaciers . . . in Scotland, Ireland and England."

Agassiz was always corresponding with other scientists, and with the help of some of them he brought out a thick and useful volume with a Latin title, *Nomenclator Zoologicus*. It was really an encyclopedia, listing alphabetically all the known kinds of animal forms, giving their proper Latin names and what were then considered their correct groupings. In the more than a hundred years since Agassiz's day so many more forms of animals have been discovered and classified, that a complete nomenclator has to be several volumes long.

During the years that he was teaching at Neuchâtel, Agassiz began to exchange letters with Charles Bonaparte, the Prince of Canino, a relative of Napoleon's. The Prince of Canino was an amateur naturalist, especially interested in birds, and one of Agassiz's countless admirers. He and Agassiz began to chat back and forth in their letters about America. The Prince was planning a trip to America, and he wanted Agassiz to go with him. The idea of going to America startled Agassiz when he was actually faced with it. The more he mulled it over in his mind the more fascinating he found it. What fossil fishes were buried in the earth layers of the American continent? What evidence of an Ice Age could he find there?

The Prince planned to go to America in another two years, in the spring of 1844, and he wrote to Agassiz to say, "I indulge myself in dreaming of the journey to America in which you have promised to accompany me. What a relaxation! and at the same time what an amount of useful work!"

It was only a dream of the Prince's.

"I wish I could accept your kind invitation," Agassiz re-

A Great Work Completed

plied, "but until I have gone to the bottom of the glacier question and terminated my *Fossil Fishes,* I do not venture to move."

His work on fossil fishes was nearing its conclusion, though. It was terminated the following year, in 1843. Ten years of writing and research had gone into the five volumes of text and their companion volumes of pictures, and a tremendous personal sacrifice. During those ten years there had been far more people eating at his table than he could afford, and the conflicts and rivalries among them had disturbed his family's peace.

Karl Vogt had sometimes tried to council Agassiz, but Agassiz would not listen. At last they quarreled, and Vogt went to Paris to find himself another post. That left Agassiz's long unfinished study on fresh-water fishes up in the air. Vogt had been working on it, and one volume had been brought out. It was one task that Agassiz never managed to finish.

Desor became more and more important in his own eyes. He had received so much generous training from Agassiz and was allowed to do so many tasks, that he began to fancy himself a research scientist. Dinkel tried to warn Agassiz about Desor, telling him that Desor was not quite so fine a person as he thought. Agassiz wouldn't take his advice either.

By the end of another year, Agassiz closed down his publishing establishment and sold his equipment. Dinkel, his close friend since college days, left to find himself other work.

Agassiz's major project in science was completed. It seemed as though this ought to be the point in his life when he could look about him for a higher-salaried post and provide more comfort for his family. But scientific research never ended for Agassiz. All of his life he would go on thinking of all the fossil and living fishes in the world that he had not yet seen, all the geography he had not yet examined for evidence of glaciers. He would never be through seeking for the best way to classify fishes. The only solution was to go on studying more and more fishes—from all over the world. The idea of going to America still persisted in his mind.

It persisted because the Prince of Canino still wrote to him about it. He even asked Agassiz to be his guest in America for the summer. It was a little more than Agassiz wanted to accept. Instead, he asked Dr. Humboldt to write to the King of Prussia, asking for a grant for Agassiz. Humboldt did so gladly.

Agassiz felt rather restless while he waited for Humboldt's report on the King's answer, and he spent more time than usual with his children.

The baby Pauline was now four, Ida was seven, and Alexander nine. Agassiz doted on Alexander. The lad was beginning to show a real interest in natural science, and in his room he kept a collection of specimens, some alive, some preserved in alcohol. If anyone approached them too closely, or seemed careless and clumsy, he called out, "Please don't touch my anatomy."

Alexander was as husky and energetic as his father, and he ran free and wild with his playmates, along the edge of the lake, or through the Jura hills. He and his friends, true to their age at nine, formed rival gangs. The gangs soon became divided according to the politics of the day: the Royalists who where loyal to the King of Prussia, and the Reds who wanted Neuchâtel to join the Swiss Confederacy.

Louis Agassiz never paid much attention to politics. He lived in a world of fins, scales, skeletons, leaf patterns, sepals, petals, granite boulders, sandstone layers, ice and permanent snows. But he naturally felt a deep personal devotion to the

A Great Work Completed

King of Prussia who had given him so much help in his scientific adventures. He was proud of his son, proud of the boy's independent spirit, proud of his leadership among the other lads of Neuchâtel—until he heard that the boy had joined the Reds and was carrying on mock warfare against the Royalists.

He even received a complaint from the Prussian Governor of Neuchâtel one day: "Your boy passed me in the street and failed to salute me."

Such rudeness and disrespect for authority had to be punished.

"You must salute the Governor!" Louis Agassiz insisted, and sulkily the boy consented.

The next time Alexander passed the Governor in the street he saluted him with so much exaggeration and so much make-believe respect that the Governor was furious. This meant more punishment at home.

The Governor was a pompous, petty fellow, and he watched for every opportunity to bear down on the Agassiz boy. When he visited the school to present prizes, he spotted Alexander and ridiculed him in front of the whole class. But the list of prizes happened to include Alexander's name, since he was a good student. With a contemptuous *humph* the Governor called out, "Alexander Agassiz."

Alexander rose to his feet, straight and proud as an Alpine peak, turned his back upon the Governor and marched from the classroom. How the young Reds cheered!

Either the King of Prussia never heard about nine-year-old Alexander's political views, or he understood young boys, which is very likely. Shortly after the incident Louis Agassiz received a letter from the King granting him fifteen thousand francs for a trip to America.

A Scientist of Two Worlds

There was only one disappointment. Now that Agassiz had his grant, the Prince of Canino had to cancel his plans, and Agassiz would have to go to America alone. But Agassiz could not remain depressed very long with such a tremendous prospect ahead of him. A whole new continent awaited him! How much exploring and investigating would he be able to do?

Sir Charles Lyell had been in America for nearly a year in 1841 and 1842, and because he was a geologist who was convinced about Agassiz's Ice Age, he looked for glacial evidence right away.

"I have already observed," Lyell had written in his diary almost at once, "several rounded boulders with one flat side scratched and furrowed, as if it had been held firmly in position when frozen into ice, and rubbed against a hard rocky bottom."

Agassiz decided to consult Lyell about the whole matter. Perhaps he would be able to give lectures in America and earn a little additional money that way. It would lengthen his visit. But what about his ability to speak English? His answer came back very quickly from Lady Lyell:

"My husband thinks your plan of lecturing a very good one, and sure to succeed, for the Americans are fond of that kind of instruction. We remember your English was pleasant, and if you have been practicing since, you have probably gained facility in expression, and a little foreign accent would be no drawback."

Did he know about the Lowell Institute in Boston, she asked. They gave courses of lectures and paid very well.

"As my husband is writing to Mr. Lowell tomorrow upon other matters, he will ask him whether there is any course still open. . . ."

A Great Work Completed

The household that had just begun to settle down, was in wild confusion once more. Plans, clothes, questions, notes, exercises in English . . .

Cecile just sighed. She could tell that her health was going downhill.

"I do not have the strength for such a long journey," she told him.

She and Agassiz decided that the wisest thing would be for her to return to her family in Karlsruhe and take the two little girls with her. Alexander was old enough to be left in school in Neuchâtel.

"I wish you could go with me," Louis Agassiz said more than once.

"I cannot."

While he corresponded with Lyell in England and Lowell Institute in Boston, Cecile began to pack. She could almost feel a little of her youthful zest coming back as she prepared to return to Karlsruhe. She had been living in Neuchâtel for nearly twelve years, struggling with poverty most of the time. Now she could go home to peace and security.

"When I return from my American tour, everything will be different. I'll make things easier for you," he promised.

In May, 1845, Cecile and her two little girls were settled in the coach ready to leave.

"I wonder," Mrs. Agassiz mused, as she waved to her husband from the coach window, "whether I shall ever see him again."

8

DISCOVERING AMERICA

LOUIS AGASSIZ felt crushed as he watched the stage disappear. Yet, how could he have avoided it? His work must go on. His research was as important to him as breathing. When anyone made contributions to the betterment of mankind, there had to be sacrifices.

That summer he made his last trip to the Aar Glacier and spent the next winter in Neuchâtel teaching, planning his lectures for the Lowell Institute, and practicing his English.

Everyone who said good-by to him—family, neighbors, students—had a premonition about it.

"Professor Agassiz is *leaving* us!"

"Only for a few months," he insisted, but they shook their heads. They had heard what a fascinating place America was.

On his last night in Neuchâtel, his students staged a torch-light parade, and sang native folk songs under his window.

He boarded the stage that went through Basle to Karlsruhe to see Cecile and his daughters once more.

Discovering America

His ship was to sail from Liverpool and on the way to Liverpool he made the rounds of his scientific friends. In Paris he was lionized. His admirers even traveled in from the provinces in the hope of meeting him.

"Stay in Paris!" they begged him. "There are many good positions available here."

He shook his head and replied, "I am on my way to America just now."

In London he saw Sir Charles Lyell and other British scientists. Lyell had returned that same spring from a second trip to the United States. He had toured the White Mountains, the New England seashore, and the Atlantic states all the way to Florida, the Gulf Coast and the Ohio and Mississippi rivers. He had seen near Portsmouth, New Hampshire, huge granite boulders that had obviously come from farther north, as well as deposits of clay and gravel. In the gravel he found fossil shells of shellfishes that were native to the Arctic. And everywhere there were rocks polished and grooved by ice.

"An Ice Age!" declared Agassiz.

"Yes," said Sir Charles. "There are numerous lakes and ponds in that region, very similar to the southern part of Norway and Sweden, and the glacial drift resembles that of Ireland and Scotland."

Agassiz went on to Liverpool determined to make every minute in America count. He must see as much as possible.

He sailed on one of the steamships of the Cunard Line, from Liverpool to Halifax and Boston. Steamships were still rather new and they carried masts and sails in case their engines should fail. Since it was late in September the weather was rough and blowy at times. But the accommodations were comfortable.

95

A Scientist of Two Worlds

"I must succeed in America," Agassiz had said to himself again and again. "I must succeed for the sake of my wife and children."

He practiced his English constantly.

"Please converse with me only in English," he said to the ship's officers and the other passengers, and soon they were all his teachers.

"I am too old to learn a new language," he would say. "I speak German fluently because I learned it when I was young, but English is another matter."

They did all they could to encourage him, and to one another they said, "Isn't his French accent charming!"

When the steamer put in at Halifax some two weeks later, the passengers bound for Boston were permitted to go ashore for a few hours. The tall, boyish, smiling Swiss scientist was among the first down the gangplank. He hurried for the open land beyond the harbor, walking fast and hard, watching the ground as he hurried along.

"The familiar signs," he reported on his return to the ship, "the furrows and scratches, the *line engraving,* so well known in the Old World. It is as I anticipated."

One more day on the water and Boston Harbor came into view. First the Cape Anne lighthouse, and soon a little sailing schooner brought the harbor pilot out to the ship. The ship continued on close to the coast, past Salem, Lynn, and Nahant. The land circles round to form a natural breakwater, and the ship passed the little town of Hull on the end of the peninsula before moving into the quiet waters of the harbor, with its many small islands. The passengers who crowded to the rail of the steamer could see the great dome of the Boston State House and the tall slim white monument that marked Bunker Hill.

Discovering America

The Cunard docks were in East Boston near the South Ferry that plied between Boston and East Boston. When Agassiz walked from the ferryboat that had brought him across the bay and stepped onto Atlantic Avenue, Boston's water-front street, he was the most excited man in Boston. He was here! Now, his next task, his next order of business, was to find Mr. Lowell.

"Where is Pemberton Square?" he asked a bystander in his heavy French accent.

It wasn't hard. He found Hanover Street quickly and strode along it right through the heart of the business district. How European the buildings looked! How English it all seemed! Where Hanover crossed Washington Street he was amazed at the crowds. He liked the energetic way that people moved about. That suited his temperament.

At last he found Pemberton Square. There around four sides of a public garden stood prim brick houses three stories high.

"There is gracious living in Boston," Agassiz decided, as he stood waiting before the door of one of the houses.

The gentleman of the house came himself, and as soon as he realized that Professor Agassiz had arrived he opened the door wide and begged him to come in. The gentleman was Mr. John A. Lowell, Trustee and Director of Lowell Institute. He was a cousin of the John Lowell who had founded the Institute, and belonged to the same family of Lowells as the American poet, James Russell Lowell.

Louis Agassiz had lost none of his ability to make friends and keep them. He and Mr. Lowell got on extremely well. Agassiz was soon dining around in Boston and going to social gatherings, meeting Bostonians, charming them with his good nature and his sincerity. Everyone was eager to meet him and hear him speak because the Lyells had written glowing letters about him. Educated Americans were very pleasant and obliging, he wrote home to say, and most hospitable. In fact, he had to resist many invitations to stay in their homes.

"I have often found it difficult to make it understood that the hotel, where I can work at my ease, suits me better. . . ."

His lectures began in Boston in December, and the first night that he appeared the Lowell Institute building on Washington Street was filled to the doors. Even though he knew that the lectures were free, he was amazed at the kind of audience he had: laborers, shopkeepers, clerks, housewives, all mingled together with students, teachers, lawyers, and doctors—to hear a talk on science. The sight thrilled him. He was the teacher who loved to teach, who would teach anyone who would listen.

He talked to his Boston audience as he talked to the fishermen beside the Lake of Neuchâtel or to his students at the Academy in Neuchâtel. They sat enchanted, completely silent for nearly two hours. They had thought it would be difficult, but Professor Agassiz had the ability to make everything clear. Even though his English was imperfect, and he had to pause now and then to search for a word, his ideas flowed like a sparkling mountain stream.

Lowell Institute was packed every time he spoke.

Between Boston lectures he investigated the countryside around Boston. He went to Springfield. "But what a country is this! All along the road between Boston and Springfield are ancient moraines and polished rocks." He took a steamer from New Haven to New York. "The Sound between Long Island and the coast of Connecticut presents a succession of cheerful towns and villages. . . . I have never seen such flocks of ducks and gulls."

98

Discovering America

He became a familiar figure at the Boston fish market—always hunting and poking around for new and interesting specimens.

By the end of December his lectures on natural science at Lowell Institute were coming to a close, but Boston would not let him stop. Very quickly a subscription was raised for a second series of lectures by Professor Agassiz—on glaciers.

"This is fine!" he thought to himself. "I have succeeded here. It is as I hoped."

He was winning converts to his Ice Age, too.

As was usual with Louis Agassiz, one thing always led to several others, until he was doing a great many tasks at once. The waters along the Atlantic Coast teemed with so many kinds of life that he began to spend his spare afternoons exploring the seashore. Before much longer he was writing a paper on starfishes.

He was living the life he had wanted to live from boyhood —the life of a traveling naturalist. America seemed limitless, as he read reports about her vast wild regions written by such explorers as Lewis and Clark, Zebulon Pike, and the very recent trips of John C. Fremont all the way through the Southern Pass of the Rocky Mountains to the West Coast. Kit Carson had been one of Fremont's guides.

His American adventures were constantly going back to his friends and family in Europe in long letters. His enthusiasm began to lure some of them across the ocean. First came one of his students, François de Pourtalès, who had helped Agassiz build his station on the Aar Glacier. Pourtalès was soon followed by Agassiz's former secretary, Edouard Desor, and others.

Agassiz began to plan. Here were his favorite assistants. Summer was coming on when he would have a vacation from lecturing and he could spend all of his time at the seashore.

A Scientist of Two Worlds

Why not have everyone under one roof? Very soon he had rented a three story brick house at the water's edge, across the bay in East Boston.

"But the rent is too high, Dr. Agassiz! It is a thousand dollars a year."

"So? It is the only sensible way to do it. The rent is unfortunate, but it will come from somewhere."

In he moved—he, his friends, books, specimens, bundles, microscopes—and soon others arrived to swell the household. Their home life, if you want to call it that, was rather confused since no one cared for housekeeping. But they were happy, and just snatched this or that or anything to eat. They went out early each morning in a small boat to dredge the sea for specimens, bringing home a tank full of marine life, hurrying it to their work tables. Often Dr. Agassiz would reach into the tank and take out a fish and begin immediately to explain it. Or he would shout, "Wait! Don't remove him. I want you to study the way he swims. Notice the way he uses his caudal fin."

The excursions of their small boat soon attracted the attention of the United States Coast Survey steamer that was cruising in the area. Dr. Alexander Bache, the Superintendent of the Coast Survey, fell under Agassiz's spell.

"Come aboard," said Dr. Bache one day. "I am going to cruise along Cape Cod. Have you visited Nantucket, Martha's Vineyard, and the Elizabeth Islands?"

Agassiz went on many trips along the coast with Dr. Bache after that. He was fascinated to learn that Dr. Bache was a great grandson of Benjamin Franklin.

Thus, Louis Agassiz's first summer in America was a particularly happy one.

From time to time more members were added to his household. Many of them were from Neuchâtel. In September the

Discovering America

most colorful—and confusing—guest arrived, the elderly and
stout Papa Christinat. Agassiz had sent for him the minute
he heard that he was in want as a result of political upsets
in the Swiss Canton of Vaud. The beloved Papa Christinat,
friend of the Agassiz family for years, had been trying to get
along in Italy and France. It was Papa Christinat who had
once given Agassiz the money to go to Paris. With the help
of friends in Europe Papa Christinat managed to reach
America and was soon keeping house for the crowd of earnest
naturalists in East Boston—more than twenty of them.

Papa Christinat spoke no English and saw no reason to
learn any so long as he could do his marketing with sign
language. Merchants standing behind their trays of fish,
baskets of vegetables, or racks of chickens soon learned to
understand him, and soon learned that he could beat down
their prices. Sometimes he insisted on driving the price
down so far that the merchants had to send Agassiz a bill for
the difference. But it was all right. Papa Christinat brought a
lot of happiness—even a little organization—into the household, and his French cooking was delicious. When an
admirer of Agassiz's sent him a live giant sea turtle, Papa
Christinat pounced upon it. A real economy! How he loved
economy! For days afterward he fed his flock on turtle soup,
turtle steak, turtle pot pie, and every other dish he could
contrive from the one creature.

Before the first snow fell in Boston, Louis Agassiz was
giving his second season of lectures at Lowell Institute, and
each evening crowds had to be turned away. From Boston
he went to other cities, New York, Albany, Philadelphia,
Charleston, South Carolina, Washington, D.C., and in each
city the same thing happened—throngs queuing up to get in,
spellbound listeners, and all sorts of invitations to social
affairs in between lectures.

101

A Scientist of Two Worlds

Many thought that his schedule was too heavy, but he himself wanted it that way. He needed to earn as much as possible to operate his large household. As his audiences listened and watched they weren't aware of any fatigue. Once he even gave an extra lecture in one city, because he felt it was needed. His audiences didn't see any signs of worry either, although that winter he was deeply worried about his wife and children. He had heard from his brother-in-law Alex Braun that Mrs. Agassiz was now confined to her bed with a lung congestion and bad cough. In her run-down condition she did not have sufficient strength to fight it.

But everyone in Boston and Cambridge, who knew Agassiz personally, knew how he doted on his family. Often in the midst of an evening's conversation he would bring out a letter from his wife about the children and read it to them. Once he was sitting chatting with Asa Gray and Henry Longfellow when he produced one of Cecile's letters.

"Listen to this. My son has just climbed the Fellenberg in the Breisgau. There is a real Swiss for you! He slept on the summit in the open air so that he could see the sun rise in the morning, and then walked all the way down. And he is only eleven!"

Agassiz's circle of personal friends included many amazing men in Boston, in Cambridge just across the Charles River where Harvard College was, and in the nearby village of Concord on Lexington Road. Dr. Asa Gray was one of Agassiz's earliest friendships in America. Dr. Gray was Professor of Natural History at Harvard, and botany was his favorite study. He did more than anyone else in his day to make the study of plant life, especially wild flowers, popular. Almost everyone owned a copy of Gray's manual, *Flora of North America.*

Discovering America

Henry Wadsworth Longfellow was another good friend of Agassiz's. Longfellow was teaching foreign languages at Harvard. He had spent a great deal of time in Europe learning French, German, Spanish, and Italian. When Agassiz arrived in New England, Longfellow had already published his famous poems, "A Psalm of Life" and "The Village Blacksmith," and was working on *Evangeline*.

In the village of Concord, not far from Cambridge, lived Ralph Waldo Emerson, the philosopher, and almost across the road from Emerson was the amazing Alcott family. Henry David Thoreau, the nature-lover, lived in Concord, too.

In Boston and the towns around Boston—Cambridge, Concord, Salem—were some of the greatest people in American letters. There was the young poet, James Russell Lowell; Oliver Wendell Holmes, who taught anatomy and physiology at Harvard and wrote satire on the side; Richard Henry Dana, who wrote *Two Years Before the Mast;* John Greenleaf Whittier, the Quaker poet, who campaigned against slavery; Nathaniel Hawthorne, the novelist; and George Ticknor, whose publishing company published just about everyone's books, and almost everyone was writing books. Louis Agassiz came to know them all.

When Sir Charles Lyell returned from America to England, he had told Agassiz that New England was an amazing place. Everyone there loved learning and respected education. And it was true. In his own letters home Agassiz could say almost what Lyell had said.

Letters that reached Agassiz from Europe brought political news as well as family news. The revolution in the Canton of Vaud that had sent Papa Christinat into exile was one small part of the disturbances taking place. While Agassiz was

A Scientist of Two Worlds

touring American cities in the winter of 1847-48, political matters were coming to a head in many countries of Europe. In February the French regime fell and the Second French Republic was declared. Uprisings in Italy, Austria, Hungary, Prussia, and even Switzerland, soon followed, all part of a movement toward more republican forms of government. Louis Agassiz's home canton of Neuchâtel was in the midst of it. He soon learned that Neuchâtel had joined the Swiss Confederacy. It was no longer under the sovereignty of Prussia. That meant an end of financial aid from the King of Prussia.

Destiny seemed to watch over Louis Agassiz. He plunged ahead into one project after another regardless of whether it seemed possible or not, and someone or something always turned up in the nick of time to help him out of his predicament. At about the time that he lost the patronage of the King of Prussia, Mr. Abbott Lawrence, a wealthy Boston merchant, was donating fifty thousand dollars to Harvard to found a scientific school.

Harvard had been watching Louis Agassiz. Harvard was always alert for great scholars and teachers.

"Now, if we can persuade Dr. Agassiz to accept a professorship in natural science, teaching zoology and geology, at the Lawrence Scientific School," said the college administrators, "we will be well on the way to having a fine school."

Agassiz did accept, to everyone's joy.

"Your salary, Mr. Agassiz, will be fifteen hundred dollars a year to start."

He had no idea how much, or how little, that was; in Swiss francs he would still not have known. Actually, it was a very small salary, even in those times.

Agassiz simply bustled off to find himself a house in Cambridge, and he settled on one in Oxford Street. By April, with the help of his assistants, he had moved his whole household into it, Papa Christinat and all. It was a splendid place to live! True, it was smaller than the house in East Boston, but there was a fine cellar for storing specimens, and the rent was only four hundred dollars a year. Henry Longfellow's house was a ten-minute walk away.

Best of all, down on the bank of the curving, quiet Charles River, there was an abandoned wooden shack that had once been a boathouse. It stood on piles set in the shallow water's edge. The college gave Agassiz permission to use it as a laboratory and storage space for his collections.

April was not over before Agassiz was saying bashfully to his employers, "If there is a little more storage space somewhere for my specimens, perhaps . . ."

There was—in the cellar of Harvard Hall.

Even before his moving and storing was completed he was zealously at work teaching young men to use their eyes, to learn directly from nature, to doubt what the books told them if it did not match their observations, to be honest enough to say, "I do not know," to wonder, to investigate, to have the courage to express new and different ideas.

Agassiz, the teacher! It was as a teacher that he made his greatest contribution in America. He taught students how to learn; he taught teachers how to teach. He brought to the schools in America something new and different and vital.

A young man came into the classroom and sat down leisurely, as so many did year after year. Professor Agassiz was just as leisurely about it. He plunged his hand down into a jar of specimens preserved in alcohol and brought out a fish, laying it on a pan in front of the student. The odor was awful.

"Take this fish and look at it; we call it a haemulon; by

and by I will ask what you have seen."

That seemed easy. In ten or fifteen minutes the young man was ready to be questioned on his knowledge of the fish. But the Professor had left the building. Oh, well, may as well look at the fish a little longer. All morning, he sat with the fish; after lunch he sat with the fish again. He must not damage it, and he must remember to sprinkle alcohol on it to prevent it from drying. At last, out of sheer boredom, he stuck his finger down the fish's throat to feel the teeth. He counted the scales and noticed how they were arranged. He had just begun to draw a picture of the fish, when his teacher returned.

"That is right," said Professor Agassiz. "A pencil is one of the best of eyes."

Then he asked the young man what he had learned, and on hearing he shook his head.

"You have not looked very carefully; why, you haven't even seen one of the most conspicuous features of the animal, which is as plainly before your eyes as the fish itself; look again, look again."

And he was gone again, leaving a miserable young man to his misery.

At the end of another day the Professor asked, "Have you seen it yet?"

No. Still, there was nothing to do but remain with the reeking fish.

Still another day, and the Professor asked once more.

"Do you perhaps mean," asked the young man, "that the fish has symmetrical sides with paired organs?"

"Of course, of course!" declared the teacher happily. "He has bilateral symmetry."

Was that all? Was the job done?

Discovering America

Oh, no, no! replied the teacher. He must go on looking at his fish. He had only begun to observe. Whenever the student looked wistfully at his teacher, the only reply he received was, "Look, look, look!"

Slowly and gradually he learned the details of the fish from his own observations. Slowly and gradually he learned to think independently, to inquire, to wonder, to compare one fish with another.

Students did not always survive Dr. Agassiz's kind of teaching. Some of them gave up in despair and fled from the laboratory. But those who stayed, never forgot what they had learned.

One young man was given the bones of a blue heron and told to assemble them correctly. But he had been out that morning collecting partly developed birds' eggs, and when he returned to the laboratory he spent his time studying the embryos in the eggs. He thought he would surely draw a scolding from Agassiz. Nothing of the sort! Agassiz was happy to see the student's interest in embryos.

"Never mind the skeleton," said Agassiz. "Go right on collecting embryo birds and making drawings."

Every student was an individual. Agassiz gave one a frog, another a starfish, still another a clam.

"Look, look, look!" was all he ever told them in the way of help.

When they had completed their observations and thought their troubles were over for a while, Agassiz handed them a second creature resembling the first and said, "Now study this one and tell me how it resembles the first and how it is different."

No student of Agassiz's ever forgot him.

9

LAKE SUPERIOR

TWO of his students had a special reason for never forgetting Agassiz. He chose them to accompany him on a tour of Lake Superior.

For a long time Agassiz had wanted to explore lower Canada, and he had had one trip to the St. Lawrence River and Niagara Falls with Mr. Lowell, a teasing sample of breath-taking, robust country abounding in glacial evidence. Now, at last, his teaching post at Cambridge had made a long, serious trip through the Great Lakes region possible. As soon as the Lawrence Scientific School closed for the summer, he planned to be off.

Sixteen men in all were going, the two students from the Lawrence School, six members of the senior class of Harvard, Jules Marcou who later wrote a life of Professor Agassiz, professors from both the Lawrence School and Harvard, and one artist, J. Elliott Cabot of Boston.

Lake Superior

Desor did not go on this trip. He had at last caused so much difficulty in the household that even the kindly Agassiz had had to ask him to leave. Desor had been with Agassiz at East Boston, but he had not come with the group to Cambridge.

Agassiz's Great Lakes party was to meet at an Albany hotel and set out from there, and many of them had already gathered when Agassiz arrived. There was a sudden happy bustle when he reached the hotel room, for they were all eagerly awaiting their teacher.

"You are just in time for tea, Dr. Agassiz."

"So?" said the Professor, and he unrolled a huge piece of black canvas that was to serve as a blackboard, and lifted handfuls of chalk from his pockets. He began his first lecture right then and lectured to them almost every day from the middle of June, when they started, to the end of August, when they arrived back. There was no thought of sparing himself, because he so earnestly wanted them to learn as much as possible.

"On the way here I saw a great variety of soil and all sorts of glacial materials—sand, polished rocks. I have never seen anywhere as in your country such a variety of trees in one forest. All in the same forest I saw oak, pine, spruce, cedar, beech, birch, chestnut, poplar, elm, ash, maple, hickory. And did you know?" and here he chuckled. "All along the way, even along the railway tracks, most of your plants and weeds are European. The native plants have been driven back with the Red Man. Lyell observed that as we go farther west the exotic plants will decrease and the native plants increase. . . . Now already you have seen three great water basins: the Atlantic Coast, the Connecticut Valley and the Hudson Valley. . . ."

A Scientist of Two Worlds

And so on and on as the party listened fascinated while this Swiss naturalist showed them what had been before their unobservant eyes all along.

Next morning they boarded a train for Buffalo, traveling up the valley of the Mohawk, past cultivated fields, log houses, dense forests, an occasional town.

"Those bright yellow flowers out there are the blossoms of the mustard," said their teacher. "They are imported, too."

Trains in the middle of the nineteenth century were rather uncomfortable and extremely sooty since the engines used soft coal, but these men were travelers and adventurers going into the wilderness. They knew there were greater discomforts ahead, and that soon they would be sleeping on the ground.

Buffalo they discovered was a mushrooming lake port, spreading along the shore of the lake, busy as a beehive with hustling stevedores constantly heaving cargo in and out of lake boats and in and out of canal barges. The Erie Canal began at Buffalo and stretched across New York State to connect with the Hudson above Albany. Buffalo was less polished and polite than Boston. In Buffalo boat whistles shrieked and stevedores shouted every hour of the day and night. Agassiz was beginning to notice something else: there were Indians mingled with the crowds.

"They are probably Iroquois," he was told.

He was beginning, too, to realize how vast a country he was visiting. They had come more than five hundred miles to reach this first lake port. All of Switzerland was not so wide.

"I want to see Niagara Falls again," he had said, and so the party crossed into Canada to see the famous cataract of water

Lake Superior

that the Niagara River made as it roared over the escarpment in its bed.

Agassiz and his companions returned to Buffalo to board a lake steamer bound for Detroit—another overnight trip. The weather was fair, the water a soft gray-green during the day, and the steamer followed the southern shore of Lake Erie. Agassiz watched the flat and monotonous shore line, with red crumbling banks and dense forests and only an occasional log hut.

"I am beginning to see the flat prairie country," he said.

Cleveland was another booming lake port. There was a long pier stretching far out into the lake, because the land was too flat for a natural harbor.

"These are truly inland seas!" said Agassiz. "And to think that there are five of them."

They were in Detroit early the next day and soon on their way again toward Lake St. Clair. Black terns flew overhead while swallows darted in and out among the flock. As the boat entered the St. Clair River that connects Lake Erie with Lake Huron it had to proceed with greatest caution. The water in the river was shallow, and the shores on either side were low and marshy. Every so often the keel of the boat touched bottom and stirred up the mud. The steamer did not emerge onto Lake Huron until breakfast time next day, and when it did Professor Agassiz was on deck.

He drew a deep breath and let it out with a happy sigh. The country was beginning to look truly different. The forests were wilder with more pine trees, and the lake water was darker. Indians passed them in canoes, and the Swiss scientist looked and looked at their features. He was beginning to notice that the tribes differed from one another.

"We are nearing the western limits of the United States,"

he was told. "The western shore of Lake Superior is bounded in part by the Minnesota Territory."

That same spring Wisconsin had been admitted to the Union, and the travelers heard it mentioned often as they went westward. But west of Wisconsin were the territories, much of them unexplored wilderness, marked "unorganized" on the maps.

"How many states are there in the Union now?" Agassiz asked.

"Wisconsin is the thirtieth, Professor."

A whole day and night passed before the lake steamer reached Mackinac Island. It pulled in to the wharf in the pouring rain.

The men had thought that they would simply move their things to another steamer that would take them through the Sault Sainte Marie, the strait connecting Lake Huron with Lake Superior.

"The Sault steamer has left," they were told.

"When is the next one?"

"Not for another week."

Professor Agassiz had no notion of wasting a whole week of their precious vacation time, and neither had anyone else.

"We will hire boats to take us," they all agreed.

They stood on the little wooden pier looking up at the town. It was a single row of sorry looking cabins and stores. Beyond, up on the ridge, were the buildings of the fort. The party stayed at the Mission House, a mean sort of hotel, for that day and one night. Hotels were becoming more and more primitive, and the travelers knew that soon there would be none and that they would have to use their camping equipment on whatever shore they found themselves at night.

Agassiz thought only of science. He watched the land

formations, the plants, the birds and fishes, the insects. He paid little attention to his accommodations or the shoddy appearance of the town. What did interest him were the Indians down on the beach hauling in fishing nets. He hurried down to them and bought some whitefish and brought it gaily back for breakfast.

"I am going out with them later," he announced.

"With whom?"

"The fishermen, of course. I have done it since I was a boy in Switzerland. That is the way to find specimens."

The botanists in the group were already comparing some exceptionally beautiful wild flowers they had gathered: pink lady's slipper, yellow honeysuckle, purplish red hound's tongue. Agassiz promptly gave their scientific names in order. "The lady's slipper belongs to the orchid family; it is Cypripedium, and you found it growing in a damp, shady place. The honeysuckle is Lonicera, sometimes called Woodbine, and it is from Europe. The third is Cynoglossum, and you found it in a dryer place, another European plant." And he was gone, trying to discover what he could about the island, its lime cliffs, its luxuriant plant life.

The island was only about three miles wide and two miles long. Around most of it ran a narrow beach. The rest of the land was high and rocky, making steep cliffs all along the beach.

True to his word, Agassiz was soon sitting in a canoe, in the pouring rain, while the Indians hauled fish from the lake. The Indians were Ojibwas, he found out, one of the Chippewa tribes. Now and again he leaned forward and pounced on one of their fish, claiming it for himself. That same afternoon his flock gathered to hear a lecture on ichthyology.

A Scientist of Two Worlds

Before him on his demonstration table he had a pike and a trout.

"This pike, or pickerel," he began, "may be found in either America or Europe." Then, holding it aloft, he described all its external characteristics: the fins—the dorsal fins or those standing up along the center of its back, the caudal or tail fin, the pectoral fins or those on its sides just behind the gills, the ventral fins placed in the center of its underside like the keel of a ship. Nothing escaped Agassiz— the shape and arrangement of the scales, the rows of teeth and how they were placed, the coloring—greenish brown above, whitish below and golden stripes on the sides.

Next, he laid the pike down, and with a skillful hand and a sharp scalpel he slit open the belly skin. "Here is the heart," he said, pointing to each organ as he identified it. "Notice how far forward it is in this species, just between the gills; and here is the air bladder, which is a rudimentary lung. Above this are the ovaries which extend from one extremity of the abdomen to the other, and behind it all is the kidney, which extends along the spine."

The trout was next.

"The trout, like the whitefish, belongs to the salmon family. Ah, this fellow makes excellent eating! Much better than the pike. This is a lake trout, biggest of the trouts. There are speckled trout, mountain trout, and rainbow trout. They all prefer the fresh-water lakes and streams. But the salmon prefers the sea and only comes up into the fresh-water rivers to spawn."

He showed them point by point first the external differences between the pike and trout, different shapes and arrangements of scales, fins and teeth, and then the internal differences.

Lake Superior

"Scales tell a great deal about a fish," he said, "such as his degree of maturity. When the salmon leaves the salt water to come up a fresh-water stream to spawn, his scales stop growing and actually lose in size."

He seemed lost in thought for a moment.

"This family," he said of the trout, "is the most difficult one among all fishes. But I have studied them so carefully that I can distinguish the European species by a single scale."

The boat the men hired to take them through the Sault was scarcely better than a mud scow. It had a square sail and spritsail, in case of a breeze, and four oarsmen and skipper. Early in the morning, the scientists loaded their gear aboard and set out, traveling northward at first, making slow progress as their happy-go-lucky oarsmen chattered in French or sang gay songs. The oarsmen were *voyageurs*, French Canadians, descendants of the earliest settlers. The voyageurs knew more than anyone else, except the Indians, about geography of the Great Lakes region.

The party reached Goose Island in time for luncheon, and went ashore to cook it over a campfire on a pebbly beach. Mackinac was still visible to the south of them. They set out again, bearing eastward, until the daylight began to fail.

The skipper advised them to camp on a little island just off the shore, but some of the party insisted that they wanted to camp on the sandy beach of the mainland. The crew would have none of it. Too many mosquitoes, they declared. Some of the naturalists insisted on going to the mainland, while the rest of the party went on to the island. Just as camp was about made on the island and the fire was beginning to burn brightly, there were cries from the mainland: "Help, help! Send the boat!" There they were, down on

115

A Scientist of Two Worlds

the beach, as close to the water as they could get, waving their arms around in the air, tying scarfs around their heads, jumping about to fight off the great clouds of mosquitoes. The voyageurs, wearing wide grins, rowed over and rescued the scientists.

They were on their way again at four o'clock in the morning, traveling among small islands, watching the densely forested shore line. Soon the bow of their boat turned northward and they passed through the narrow strait between the mainland and Drummond's Island, then westward toward St. Joseph's Island.

As the bow of their boat turned in to the shore and ran up on the beach, they noticed a tall man, unshaven, carelessly dressed, walking down toward them. They expected him to be unfriendly, but instead he invited them to luncheon. As soon as Professor Agassiz had introduced himself and his companions, the man said, "Oh, yes indeed! I know of you, Professor Agassiz."

The man had been a major in the British army and had retired. He had bought the entire island so that he and his wife and children could have a peaceful place to live. In his house were shelves and shelves of books, and he was extremely well informed on natural science. The conversation all during luncheon was lively and sparkling.

"I have something I hope you will accept," the major said, and he presented Professor Agassiz with a rare fish, the garpike of Lake Huron, preserved in alcohol. The garpike is one of the few remaining examples among living fishes of the ancient ganoids, which Dr. Agassiz had mentioned in his *Fossil Fishes*.

Agassiz was delighted, and he held the jar aloft. "Soon we shall have a lesson on this ancient, primitive fellow!"

Lake Superior

The travelers found it difficult to leave such an interesting host, but it was necessary. They were in their boat again, gliding along not far from the shore. They were really moving into the channel of the Sault now, and when evening arrived they camped on another small island, rolling up in their blankets on the ground and trying to protect themselves as much as possible from the ferocious mosquitoes. They were all grateful for the morning.

Another long day on the water took them through a widened portion of the strait called Lake George and a shallow portion called Mud Lake. Then ahead of them they saw the Lower Rapids of the Sault, where the water rushed and churned through a narrow rocky stretch. The oarsmen had a difficult time guiding their boat, and it scarcely seemed to make any progress at all.

But as the swift current ended and the stream widened again, the men saw the two villages of Sault Sainte Marie, one on the Canadian side and one in Michigan.

The village on the American side, where the travelers planned to spend a couple of days before going on, was merely a few log huts, and behind them a fort. Along the one street strolled voyageurs, traders, Indians. Nobody was busy, nobody was in a hurry; some men lounged on wooden chairs in front of the huts, dangling big cigars from their mouths. Beyond the village in every direction were forests, forests, forests.

"This is certainly the wilderness now," the men all agreed.

On the Canadian side stood a building belonging to the Hudson's Bay Company. It did not take Agassiz long to discover that the company had scientists stationed there to make a geological survey of the area. The company was interested in the copper mining possibilities of the region, and one of

117

A Scientist of Two Worlds

the men showed Dr. Agassiz a map of the entire Lake Superior full of notations on its geology.

"I can share a discovery with you," Dr. Agassiz said, showing them some welts on the back of his hand.

The company men laughed. "Oh, yes. That is from our black fly."

The black fly was proving one of Mother Nature's less pleasant inventions. Travelers in the Lake Superior region had to tighten their collars and button their gloves, for a black fly could wriggle in and draw blood where a mosquito would not dream of going. Professor Agassiz soon had one in his power, examining it under a lens. "Let me see, now. Smaller than the housefly and blacker, white spots on his legs, a fast traveler . . ."

Suddenly the professor cocked his head at a new sound. It was the song of a bird that he had not heard before.

"The opening note sounds something like the European nightingale," he observed. "What bird is that?"

"That is the white-throated sparrow, Professor Agassiz. The swamps here are full of them. It is the male sparrow that you hear."

After four days at Sault Sainte Marie, Louis Agassiz and his companions packed all their gear and collections into long birchbark canoes, covering each load with buffalo robes, and set out for Lake Superior. They had to traverse a few rapids above the falls before they reached smooth water, but their paddlers were voyageurs and Ojibwa Indians. They were in skillful hands.

By evening they were beyond the narrow channel of the Sault and almost at their goal—Lake Superior. The scientists felt quite festive as they sat around their campfire watching

118

Lake Superior

wild birds roast on spits. Before daylight they rolled out of their blankets and were back into their canoes in record time.

The channel grew wider and wider until the two shores were more than five miles apart. Then it narrowed again, and their canoes passed between two peninsulas: Point Iroquois on their left and Gros Cap on their right. As the canoes glided between these two points, the men knew they were at last on Lake Superior. Whitefish Bay spread out before them, and beyond the bay the vast lake.

"So!" Agassiz half whispered as he gazed at the expanse of glistening, crystal clear water, the largest fresh-water lake in the world.

The men spent the whole month of July traveling along the northern shore of Lake Superior, camping on the beach at night, exploring up rivers, collecting specimens of every natural thing. So engrossed were they in this amazing wild world that no amount of black flies and mosquitoes could stop them.

The geography of Lake Superior was different from the other Great Lakes. It was more rugged; its shore lines were high and rocky and grew rockier as they went along. Cliffs sometimes rose right out of the water, broken here and there with coves and inlets. Sometimes there was a pebble beach along the water's edge.

Louis Agassiz, the geologist, was still hunting for proof of his Ice Age. And he found plenty of proof. There was no doubt in his mind that the Great Lakes had once been covered by a thick layer of ice moving down from the north then retreating and leaving behind its accumulation of gravel, or drift, and long deep scratches on the rocks.

"Look, look!" he called one day.

A Scientist of Two Worlds

They were camping on the Canadian shore of Mica Bay, and he had gone exploring on foot. Several of the naturalists hurried to see his discovery and found him pointing to a huge flat rock, at least six hundred feet across, lying near the water's edge, tilted gently northward.

"See the scratches on its surface! It has been ground down by a mighty force."

It had indeed, and many of the scratches lay about in a north-south direction.

We know most of the geological story of the Great Lakes at last, and the knowledge would have thrilled Agassiz. He was entirely right in supposing that a great ice sheet had once covered the region of the Great Lakes. The ice pushed down four different times during the four cold periods. But long before the Ice Age, millions of years before it, the Great Lakes region had been under the sea. While it was under the sea, its layers of sandstone and limestone formed. Then, as the earth's surface continued to change, the sea bottom was raised above the surface, and the sea drained away. Then came the period of great glaciers, pushing down into Minnesota, Michigan, Wisconsin, Indiana, New York, Pennsylvania, Ohio. It is thought that the ice in places may have been six miles thick, and that would have made it terrifically heavy. Sometimes it pushed forward several feet a day. And as it moved forward, it gouged and scooped. As the earth turned warmer and the glacier retreated, there was left a great inland sea covering most of the Great Lakes region except Lake Erie. But the land continued to rise, ever so slowly, until the great inland sea was broken up into smaller ones—the present lakes.

The Swiss Professor and his companions made several excursions up rivers as they came to them, noting the geology and collecting plant and animal specimens. The Montreal River, they found, was wide, and had built up a delta at its mouth. The lake water there was so clear they could see all the way to the bottom, even though it was quite deep. When they stopped at the Toad River to make camp, canoes full of Indians came out to greet them and sell them fish.

"Boojou! Boojou!" called the Indians, meaning *bonjour,* the French for good day.

The men explored about a quarter of a mile up the Toad River.

Wild plants seemed to be at the height of their color. Bright orange lichens colored the forest in splashes. There were lilies, purple onion blossoms, and small wild flowers. The trees here were spruce, balsam fir, birch and aspen.

"The white pines and maples have disappeared," the Professor noted.

They were off again at sunrise, and their next river was the Michipicoten. In its harbor there was a Hudson's Bay Company post and a small settlement, and that gave the travelers a chance to chat with men who knew the countryside.

In the days that followed, the course of the explorers took them past hills, coves, sloping rocks, high cliffs, waterfalls, and steep palisades. Now and again an Indian village showed in the trees. For several nights they watched the northern lights in the sky.

On the twentieth of July they saw, looming tall ahead of them, Thunder Cape. It was a noble mountain headland, rising almost vertically, with forests about its base. The lake around it seemed dotted with hundreds of little islands.

Agassiz and his friends knew they were nearing the western limits of the lake. Soon their voyage would be over. Beyond

A Scientist of Two Worlds

Thunder Cape, in Thunder Bay, was Fort William, their last port of call.

After they had glided past the tip of Thunder Cape, they could see the white buildings of the fort on the distant mainland, and before the sun had set they were ashore, being welcomed, handed a big bundle of mail that had been forwarded to them, and led to quarters where they could bathe and shave with hot water. For they were a dirty, grizzly crowd of men after their long camping-canoeing journey in the Canadian wilderness.

They stayed at Fort William and neighboring places for nearly a week, but their vacation was almost gone.

"I wish I could spend a few weeks on Isle Royale," said Agassiz, dreaming of all the possibilities for collecting on the huge island that stood in Lake Superior just beyond Thunder Cape.

His companions nodded. They would have gone with him at the drop of a hat. But they all knew that time was running out and that they must return to their studies and jobs. What a vacation it had been! How many students of natural science would ever be able to boast of having spent a whole summer touring the Great Lakes with Professor Agassiz?

Professor Agassiz, with his students, fellow professors, one artist, four barrels and twelve large boxes full of specimens, started home over about the same route they had come by: to Michipicoten, Mica Bay, the Sault Sainte Marie, Lake Huron and Lake Erie. From Lake Erie on, the railroad officials had quite a time with all the barrels and boxes.

Louis Agassiz's friends were waiting for him with sober faces when he reached Cambridge the end of August. Papa Christinat, Arnold Guyot who very recently had come to

Lake Superior

America to join the household, and all his other guests and tenants, gathered about him—to help him with his bags, to take his coat, to fix him some hot coffee.

"What is the matter?" he asked, looking from one to another.

"We have some unfortunate news for you, Professor Agassiz."

"A letter came, Professor Agassiz, from your brother-in-law, Alex Braun."

"Well?" he demanded.

"The letter came while you were traveling homeward, and we could not reach you. It is about your wife. She has died, Professor Agassiz, and we are all very, very sorry."

His sunny face clouded over, and his eyes filled with tears. Cecile was young! He had realized she was ill, but not that ill.

"Tell me," he said in a low voice as he sank into a chair.

It had been the consumption, they said. When she began to realize that she could not recover, she asked to have her children with her. She had died on the twenty-seventh of July, just as the travelers were beginning their homeward trek. The children were still with Alex Braun.

"You know," said Agassiz, "my wife was a fine artist. Did I show you the pictures she drew of the children just recently?"

They had already seen the pictures, but they looked at them all over again.

"Yes," said Louis Agassiz, "she was an artist, a very good artist, and a very devoted wife, too."

10

THE SECOND MRS. AGASSIZ

AGASSIZ controlled his grief by keeping busy. He had his students at Lawrence School who needed his attention. There would have to be a book about Lake Superior. He must begin work on volume two of a book he had just recently published, *Principles of Zoology*. He and Dr. A. A. Gould had written it together. Of course, his lectures . . . And, above all else, the specimens he had brought back from the Great Lakes must all be sorted out and studied and classified.

What of his children? He wrote to his brother-in-law and asked him to take care of Alexander for a while longer and to send the two little girls to their grandmother in Switzerland. "I plan to bring them all over to America eventually," he told everyone.

Those who knew the state of affairs in his house on Oxford Street held their tongues and hoped for the best. Agassiz had

The Second Mrs. Agassiz

twenty-three persons living with him, and there were mat-
tresses spread around on the floors to accommodate them.
Papa Christinat was keeping house in his usual way, and
everyone was saving specimens of plants and animals, dead
and alive. Agassiz so earnestly wanted to have his children
with him, though, that during the winter and spring that
followed many of his friends in Cambridge—the Lowells,
Professor Felton of the Harvard faculty, and others—decided
to help him arrange passage for thirteen-year-old Alexander.

Louis Agassiz's good nature and smiles began to show again
at the prospect of seeing his son.

"My boy used to be very mischievous! He was in politics
when he was only nine. I hope his interest in science has
overcome that. But, however . . ."

"Does your son know any English, Professor Agassiz?"

"No, but his Latin is proficient. He will be able to use it
to communicate with the boys at the Cambridge High School
here."

Alexander Agassiz arrived in June, almost a year after
Cecile Agassiz's death, and all of Professor Agassiz's New
World friends took the boy to their hearts at once. He proved
to be a handsome lad, rather quiet and withdrawn. Like his
father, Alexander was skillful with languages. He chattered
in French and German with Papa Christinat and the other
Europeans in the house on Oxford Street, and managed with
his Latin at school until he could master some English.

But the wives of Agassiz's friends were not content with the
situation. Mrs. Felton in particular decided that Papa
Christinat was no substitute for wife and mother, no matter
how good his intentions.

Mrs. Felton had been Mary Cary of Temple Place, Boston.
The more she considered Louis Agassiz the more she thought

A Scientist of Two Worlds

of her unmarried sister Elizabeth Cary. When Louis Agassiz had first come to Boston, the mother of Elizabeth and Mary Cary had thought of the same thing. Mrs. Cary had been to church one Sunday morning where she saw Louis Agassiz sitting with the Lowells. She had come home beaming with an idea.

"Elizabeth," she had said, "the man I saw in the Lowells' pew this morning is the first person I ever saw whom I should like you to marry."

Both daughters had laughed at the time. "Oh, no, Mother!" they said. "That was Professor Agassiz, and he has a wife and three children in Europe."

"Now," said Mary Cary Felton to herself three years later, "he has three motherless children scattered all over the globe."

She arranged a dinner party, inviting her sister Elizabeth and Professor Agassiz, and presided happily at the head of the table as she watched Elizabeth and Agassiz striking up a friendship right away. During the next few weeks she held her breath as she watched the friendship deepen into love.

Whenever Agassiz came home to the house on Oxford Street, glowing with happiness after a visit with Elizabeth, Papa Christinat would shake his head and throw up his hands.

"No, no, no! This will not do. She is not for you, Agassiz. She has no money. You need a rich wife. You cannot afford to add any more dependents to this household. You are overworking as it is. It is not practical; forget her."

Agassiz had never learned the word "practical."

Elizabeth Cary was attractive, intelligent, charming, and, like her whole family, she was cultured and dignified. She was slim and graceful with hazel eyes and brown hair that

The Second Mrs. Agassiz

she wore parted in the middle with a cluster of curls over each ear.

"Ah, yes," Agassiz added, "and she has a merry laugh."

During the winter he visited with Elizabeth Cary as often as his work would permit, and she came to Cambridge to be with her sister, Mrs. Felton, as often as she could.

They were married the next spring, on April 25, 1850, when Agassiz had been a widower nearly two years. The ceremony was held at King's Chapel in Boston, the home church of the Carys on Tremont Street, not far from Temple Place, and it was a grand affair. The Carys were important socially in Boston, and the church was filled with fashionable people for the occasion.

"Lizzy looked lovely," wrote one of the bride's friends. "She was dressed in green silk, with a white camel's hair shawl, and a straw bonnet trimmed with white feathers on each side."

When the celebrations were all over, Louis and Elizabeth Agassiz drove in their carriage across the Charles River to the house on Oxford Street. There Elizabeth Cary Agassiz began at once to bring order out of confusion.

Most of Agassiz's tenants had very considerately left the house to make way for the second Mrs. Agassiz. Even Papa Christinat announced that he was going to New Orleans to live near some of his French-speaking friends.

"But I want you to stay, Mr. Christinat," said Mrs. Agassiz, realizing that he could help her learn the Professor's little likes and dislikes.

Papa Christinat would not hear of it, and he was soon off. Only one tenant remained. He was an artist named Jacques Burkhardt who was working with Professor Agassiz on his books and short scientific papers.

A Scientist of Two Worlds

Louis Agassiz began to have a well-ordered home life. Young Alexander found his stepmother sympathetic and understanding, and they were soon fast friends.

"She has begun to seem like a real mother already," Alexander said in a very few weeks.

"Now we must send for your sisters," said Elizabeth Agassiz, and the two girls—thirteen-year-old Ida and nine-year-old Pauline—were in Cambridge by the end of the summer.

"Ha, so!" declared Agassiz happily. "Did a man ever have more good fortune than I?"

Four years ago he had come to America for a visit, and as he saw his children and Elizabeth around him he knew that it was to be his home for the rest of his life.

His book, *Lake Superior,* was completed; it had come out about the time of his marriage. From time to time he published a paper on the life of some animal he was studying: Crustaceans, jellyfish, eels, embryos of insects, mollusks, coloration of animals. One of his papers was called, "The Diversity of Origin of the Human Races." There were so many types of people on the face of the earth that Agassiz, like most naturalists, spent time thinking about the question of their origins. As he observed American Negroes and the various Indian tribes, he felt that they must all have developed separately in different parts of the world.

Another of his scientific concerns was the lack of a museum at Harvard. His own collections were growing continually. Some were stored in the shack down on the Charles River, others were here and there. Harvard College had begun to pay Agassiz four hundred dollars a year for the care of his collections, since he couldn't manage such an expense himself.

"The Lawrence Scientific School ought to buy the collec-

The Second Mrs. Agassiz

tion from Agassiz and be responsible for the care of it," said some of Agassiz's friends, and they began a subscription. But subscriptions are slow affairs, and a museum of zoology was many years away. Meanwhile, Harvard provided a wooden building on the campus, considerably larger than the shack on the bank of the Charles. Agassiz was able to move his ever growing collections to larger quarters.

That winter Dr. Alexander Bache, Superintendent of the Coast Survey, invited Dr. Agassiz to go on an exploring trip among the Florida Keys and reefs, and that sent him striding happily around the house. Some more American geography! What would he find this time? America was fabulous.

Charles Darwin had published a book, *The Structure and Distribution of Coral Reefs,* several years before. In it he had made some amazing observations about the work of corals in helping to design the earth's surface. Darwin had discovered that corals liked to live at a particular depth of water. When the water above them became too deep for comfort, the corals built their tube-like shells up and up until they were where they wanted to be. What made the water above them grow deeper? Darwin decided that the land to which the corals were attached must be sinking with infinite slowness. One more item in the slow continuous history of the earth as Lyell had described it! Some lands sinking in one place and rising in another.

Agassiz was eager to make his own observations on the soft-bodied little sea animals, called polyps, with the ability to secrete their own calcium carbonate. Over the centuries corals worked diligently to create reefs and atolls and enlarge islands.

Alexander, fifteen by now, grew excited and showed plainly that he wanted to go along. His father shook his head

A Scientist of Two Worlds

and patted the boy's shoulder.

"Not this time; not yet," he said, "but some day."

And so in January Agassiz was off for ten weeks, among the coral reefs and atolls, the everglades, the Tortugas, and all their brilliantly colored wildlife, the birds, the fishes, the palms and ferns, the flowering plants.

"I have spent a large part of the winter in Florida," he wrote to Sir Charles Lyell on his return, "with a view of studying the coral reefs. I have found that they constitute a new class of reefs, distinct from those described by Darwin. . . . I have lately read a paper upon that subject before the American Academy, which I shall send you as soon as it is printed. The case is this. There are several concentric reefs separated by deep channels; the peninsula of Florida itself is a succession of such reefs, the everglades being the filled-up channels, while the hummocks were formerly little intervening islands. . . . The Tortugas are a real atoll, but formed without the remotest indication of subsidence [sinking of the earth]. . . . One of the most remarkable peculiarities of the rocks in the reefs of the Tortugas consists in their composition; they are chiefly made up of Corallines, limestone algae, and, to a small extent only, of real corals. . . ."

Thus scientists on both sides of the ocean advised one another of their findings.

Of course, with every new finding that Agassiz made, his world-wide reputation increased. Colleges and universities vied with one another for his services. Every once in a while he declined an interesting offer.

"I like it in Cambridge. I am happy here. I love my teaching."

However, in the early autumn of 1851, a little more than

The Second Mrs. Agassiz

a year after his second marriage, an invitation came that he and his wife talked over very carefully. They decided to accept it. The Medical College of the State of South Carolina, in Charleston, offered him a professorship. He need only lecture during December, January and February, they explained, the period in between his fall and spring courses at Cambridge.

Agassiz took his whole family with him to Charleston that winter—his wife and son and two daughters—as well as James Burkhardt and two laboratory assistants. He was required to give only three lectures on anatomy a week, and that left the rest of his time free for his beloved research.

He was as popular in Carolina as he had ever been in Switzerland, France, Germany, England and Massachusetts. One Carolinian lady owned a summer cottage on Sullivan's Island, and she turned it over to Agassiz and his co-workers for their laboratory. Of course, he overdid it. He could not quite realize that he did not have to learn every creature in the ocean in one season. He added popular evening lectures to his program, as well as many social invitations. Elizabeth Agassiz could see that the mild climate of the Carolinas was too enervating for a man from the Swiss mountains. She was glad when the three months were up and she could take him back to Cambridge.

There was an important prize awaiting him on his return, for his work on fossil fishes. It was the Prix Cuvier, recently established by the Academy of Sciences of the Institute of France, to be awarded once every three years for work on fossils, comparative anatomy or zoology. The first award went to Louis Agassiz in 1851. His mother had written him the happy news, because she could remember better than anyone how much work and worry and sacrifice he had put

A Scientist of Two Worlds

into those volumes. "This has given me so much happiness, dear Louis, that the tears are in my eyes as I write it to you," said her letter.

He and his family returned to Charleston for a second winter season, but they were scarcely settled when Louis Agassiz became seriously ill with a fever. He spent nearly his whole three months recuperating.

"I think we shall not come down here next winter," said Mrs. Agassiz, and he nodded. She could see that he had something else in mind, and she waited for him to give her a clue.

"You know, my dear, I think that returning by boat would be much easier than in carriages and trains."

She laughed. She knew perfectly well that he wanted to explore the Mississippi River. So she planned their return trip by the long roundabout way through New Orleans and St. Louis. It was far from being the easiest way home, because before he finished planning he decided to give lectures in each city that he came to.

Mrs. Agassiz didn't interfere with his plans to lecture. She knew how interesting the scientific talks would be to the audiences, because she realized how much she enjoyed them herself. She was glad that Alexander had chosen science as his field and was going to specialize in engineering. He had entered Harvard in the fall of 1851 and was already pulling bow on the college crew. Alexander was not overly tall, but he had a powerful physique like his father.

Back in Cambridge the Agassizes settled down once more in their house on Oxford Street, settled down as best they could, that is, in a house that had grown too small. Professor Agassiz's library alone needed more space. He didn't really know how many books he had accumulated, but the total was up in the thousands, and he was still collecting.

Many besides themselves realized that the house was too small. In 1854 Harvard College built him an ample house on Quincy and Harvard Streets, directly across from the home of the Feltons. That made it very easy for the two sisters, Mrs. Felton and Mrs. Agassiz, to visit back and forth.

The new house was as lovely as it was large, a square frame structure three stories high.

"I have my own personal reason for being glad for the new house," said Mrs. Agassiz.

"So? Why?"

"I have two daughters to launch," she said proudly.

Ida was seventeen, and Pauline was thirteen.

"I do not know anything about the launching of young ladies," said Professor Agassiz. "It is fortunate that you are with us."

11

WHEN SCIENTISTS
DISAGREE

A LARGER HOUSE was going to prove more costly to operate, and Professor Agassiz's salary at the Lawrence Scientific School was still only fifteen hundred dollars a year. His popular evening lectures in other cities had earned the extra money his family needed, but since his Carolina illness he was no longer robust enough to do strenuous traveling.

Elizabeth Cary Agassiz was realistic and practical. She knew something had to be done, and she decided that she would do it. She did not tell her husband about her plans right away, but she did talk to Alexander and Ida.

"Mother, you've never worked in your life!" said one.

"Oh, no!" said the other. "I don't think you can. You've never taught. You've never even been to public school. You said yourself that you had a private tutor as a girl!"

"I can and I will!" she declared flatly, "and you are both going to help me. When your father learns about it, he will want to help, too. But don't tell him just yet."

She had decided to open a select school for young ladies, converting the top floor of their ample house into classrooms. The plans that she explained to her stepchildren and to her friends were so competent that they were all soon convinced and helping her start her project.

When she finally told Louis Agassiz, he stared in amazement—but only for one moment. In the next moment he was wildly enthusiastic. It was a marvelous idea, marvelous!

"I shall myself superintend the methods of instruction," he said.

There were to be no lifeless routines. The teaching was to be alive, and—something practically unheard of in those times—the young ladies were to be instructed in physical geography, natural history, and botany.

"I shall lecture every day, and use specimens, models, maps and drawings. And a blackboard! There must be a blackboard."

The school was a complete success, and the Agassizes were able to stop worrying about money matters. Mrs. Agassiz kept her school for eight years, and the fame of its instruction spread. Parents sent their children to it from all over the United States. And no wonder! Louis Agassiz, Alexander and Ida Agassiz, and several Harvard professors were doing the teaching.

Not having to travel, Agassiz was able to find time for another project that had been developing in the back of his mind. His teaching of young people, the huge audiences of adults who gathered to hear his lectures on science, the increasing popularity of science in America—due largely to Dr. Asa Gray and himself—made him realize that another massive writing project was needed. Yes, Americans needed a complete book on the natural history of their own country.

Agassiz had mentioned it first in a conversation with Mr. Francis C. Gray, a Boston business man. Mr. Gray nodded his head and one word had led to another. Professor Agassiz soon published an outline or prospectus of his proposed work, *Contributions to the Natural History of the United States,* in ten volumes, at $12.00 per volume. Mr. Gray did not allow Agassiz to involve himself in the debts he had incurred with his volumes on fossil fishes. Instead, Mr. Gray himself handled the financial end of it, and he decided to obtain enough advance subscriptions to protect Agassiz against loss.

"If we can obtain five hundred subscribers," they agreed, "we can do it."

In a matter of a few weeks they had twenty-five hundred, and more continued to come in.

"Amazing, amazing!" sighed Agassiz as he set to work. America was a remarkable place. "There is not a class of learned men here, distinct from the other cultivated members of the community. On the contrary, so general is the desire for knowledge, that I expect to see my book read by operatives, by fishermen, by farmers, quite as extensively as by the students in our colleges, or by the learned professions."

To encourage him still further he received a letter from his beloved teacher, Humboldt, now in his eighties, telling Agassiz how pleased he was about the important new work he was beginning. "I am charged by the King of Prussia, who knows the value of your older works, and who still feels for you the affectionate regard which he formerly expressed in person, to request that you will place his name at the head of your long list of subscribers."

When Scientists Disagree

Now all of Agassiz's powers of knowing, remembering, observing and classifying were called into action. As of old, he gave the task his whole self. "For weeks he wrote many hours of the day and a great part of the night," his wife recalled later, "going out sometimes into the darkness and the open air to cool the fever of work, and then returning to his desk again. He felt himself that the excitement was too great."

The first part of his book was to be a long essay on the classification of the animal kingdom. Agassiz had deep feelings on this subject, and he wanted to set them all down carefully. There was one great plan in nature, and all the kinds of plants and animals belonged to it. Each species had its own characteristics, and these could not be changed. He felt that all the species had been created separately even though they were all closely related. The second part was to be about North American Testudinata. Testudinata are the turtles and tortoises, and they are an order of reptiles. Logically, the third part was to be about the embryology of the turtle, that is, the whole growth of the turtle from the time the egg is laid.

Agassiz enlisted anyone and everyone to complete his research for his *Natural History of the United States*. It could only be valuable if it was complete. When he came to his study of turtle eggs, he found that he was missing one part of the story, the earliest hours of the development of the egg.

In Middleboro, some thirty miles south of Cambridge, he knew there was a large pond inhabited by turtles, and he also knew that the young man who was principal of the academy there was something of a naturalist.

"Do you suppose you could bring me some freshly laid turtle eggs—no more than three hours old?" Agassiz asked the young man, and the latter agreed.

A Scientist of Two Worlds

"They lay their eggs some time in June. I shall begin watching for them the latter part of May."

True to his promise the young teacher got into his horse-drawn carriage every morning at dawn and drove to the pond; with a bucket of sand ready he walked to a good vantage point and sat down to wait. He knew that if the turtle did not appear by class time she would not be up that day. He had a fine schedule worked out. When she did lay her eggs, he would scoop them into his pail, dash for his carriage, drive at top speed to the railway station, catch the morning express train to Boston, and then hurry in a cab to Cambridge. If luck were with him, he could deliver the eggs to Agassiz before they were three hours old.

Morning after morning he kept his vigil, for nearly a month, until one morning late in June a huge female turtle came up out of the pond. The teacher scrambled to his feet, pail of sand in hand, and began to follow her cautiously. She climbed up on the shore and slowly made her way across a pasture into a corn field. There she pawed the ground until she found a soft sandy spot and gradually began to bury herself tail first. As soon as she had finished laying her eggs and had moved away, the young naturalist was upon the eggs, placing them gently in his pail. He ran to his carriage, leaped in, and began to speed toward the railway station. Suddenly to his horror he realized that this was Sunday. There was no express train. But a freight was coming; so he drove right onto the track in front of it. Trains ran slowly enough a hundred years ago to be stopped in that way. The freight stopped and he leaped into the cab of the engine, panting and trying to explain that he must deliver turtle eggs to Agassiz. Of course, the fireman and engineer thought he was insane, and they humored him, planning to turn him

138

over to the authorities when they reached Boston. But the minute the freight slowed down in the Boston station, he was off and into a cab, galloping over the bridge to Cambridge, through the center of Cambridge to Quincy Street and Agassiz's house.

"Quick, quick!" he said to the maid as soon as the door opened.

Right behind her was Agassiz in bathrobe and slippers.

"Let him in! Let him in! He has my turtle eggs!" said Agassiz, and seizing the pail he hurried off to his laboratory.

The eggs had been delivered in one minute less than three hours.

Such incidents were always happening. Mrs. Agassiz had grown used to surprises very early in her married life. She was groping around the floor of her closet one night, looking for slippers without bothering to light a candle, when her hand suddenly touched something cold and alive that darted away from her. She leaped back and shrieked, "There's a snake in my closet!"

"Oh, yes," said Agassiz. "I brought in several in my handkerchief last night; probably they have escaped. I wonder where the others are."

And there were ten volumes to be written about America's wildlife! These happenings would go on for years, and they did.

Another evening when Mr. and Mrs. Agassiz had guests for dinner, a bear cub of the Professor's broke loose and came lumbering into the dining room. The guests fled in terror, peeking back through the door to watch the bear eating all the food on the table.

Volume I of *Natural History* was ready for the printer in the spring of 1857. It contained Agassiz's long essay on classification, and the section on American Testudinata. There were no pictures in Volume I, he explained in the front matter, but readers would find thirty-four plates in Volume II as well as his findings on the embryology of the turtle. In Volumes III and IV Americans would read about radiates.

The year 1857 was a banner one for Louis Agassiz. Not only were there parties in honor of his fiftieth birthday, but that spring his son completed two years of graduate work at Lawrence Scientific School with a very high honor, *summa cum laude*. Soon after, Professor Agassiz's father-in-law, Thomas Cary, presented him with a summer cottage and laboratory on the northeast shore of Nahant, Massachusetts, a rocky peninsula just north of Boston. The Agassizes shared the cottage with the Feltons. There Agassiz could spend his summers studying marine animals.

Even though his work took him off by himself for long days and hours, Agassiz was a sociable fellow who loved the company of interesting people. A year or so earlier he and a few others had fallen into the habit of having dinner with Emerson at the Albion in Boston each Saturday, Emerson's day in town. There were eleven of them at first, including Agassiz, Emerson, and young Lowell. They began to call themselves "The Saturday Club," and soon Holmes, Longfellow, Whittier, and Hawthorne joined. It was at a dinner of The Saturday Club that Longfellow first read his poem, "The Fiftieth Birthday of Agassiz."

Conversations at the Club were brilliant and about almost everything under the sun. As the eighteen fifties passed and the eighteen sixties approached, the conversations were oftener and oftener about slavery. The Abolitionist movement in America was growing stronger and more widespread, and so were the bitter feelings about it. Most of the club members were Abolitionists.

When Scientists Disagree

To Agassiz the question of slavery was new, and he felt deeply troubled about it. His friend Charles Sumner, a United States Senator, was leading the crusade for abolition in the United States Senate. Bronson Alcott had lost his school in Boston because he had insisted on having a Negro student. Everyone was disturbed. In his paper, "The Diversity of Origin of the Human Races," Agassiz had said that he saw the unity of all human beings everywhere, but he also saw tremendous differences. He had concluded that while they all belonged to the human family they were different "species." In writing it he had been merely sharing his thoughts with other scientists as he was attempting to think the thing through. But feelings were becoming so tense in America on the question of race, that some unscientific people accused him of favoring slavery. The accusation distressed him deeply. He did not care for politics and did not want to become involved in political debates. Race was simply one of the secrets that Mother Nature still withheld from him, and he was trying to unravel her secret.

Charles Darwin in England was writing a book along these lines. Scientists everywhere, including Agassiz, were awaiting it eagerly. If Agassiz's suspicions about Darwin's ideas were correct, he was going to have to disagree with Darwin.

Meanwhile he concentrated on his natural history volumes, his teaching, and his collections. He was worried about his collections. He still did not have space enough to arrange them so that students and researchers could use them.

In handling the business arrangements for Agassiz's natural history volumes, Francis C. Gray had grown to love and respect Louis Agassiz deeply. None realized how deeply until Gray's death at the end of 1858. When Gray's will was read it was discovered that he had left fifty thousand dollars

A Scientist of Two Worlds

to establish a museum of comparative zoology at Harvard. But, his will specified, these funds were to be used for the purchase of specimens, not buildings. He knew the first and most important collection they would have to purchase would be that of Dr. Agassiz.

Agassiz still wept easily, just as he had done as a young man, and Gray's bequest moved him to frank tears. This was wonderful! A miracle! All that was needed—how like Agassiz—all that was needed was sufficient money to erect a building. He set about at once to raise the necessary funds.

"I shall apply to the state government," he said, since that was how it was usually done in Europe. Hadn't the patronage of the King of Prussia made his trip to America possible?

"You can't apply to the state government," he was told. "You won't get anything out of them. The members of the Massachusetts Legislature are hardheaded farmers on the whole. You'll never persuade them to spend any money on pure science. They are too practical."

Practical? What was that? Agassiz just turned his charm on full force, captivating first the governor of the state and then the State Committee on Education. Before he was through the State Legislature appropriated a hundred thousand dollars. Francis Gray's bequest had touched off a chain reaction. Private donations began to pour in until another seventy-one thousand dollars had been added. Soon Harvard College donated a piece of land.

"We are going to build a fireproof building," Agassiz told everyone, "five stories high. The main part will be 364 feet long and 64 feet wide, and the wings will be 205 feet long and 64 feet wide."

It was necessary to persuade Louis Agassiz that the funds he had raised would build just about two fifths of that. It would provide four rooms to a floor and five floors. The rest of the structure could be added in later years. That was all right with Agassiz. All he really cared about was that there *was* to be an adequate, fireproof building at last, one that would afford room for arranging and displaying specimens properly as well as for the thousands of books that were as necessary as the specimens.

Francis Gray's will had been read in December. By the following June Professor Agassiz and a host of friends were present to witness the laying of the cornerstone of the new building.

"Will you spend your summer watching the workmen?" someone asked Professor Agassiz jokingly.

"Ah! That would be fine. But I have promised my wife that we will go to Europe."

It was true. The Agassizes had at long last been able to plan a summer vacation in Europe, and they were to sail a few days after the laying of the cornerstone. Professor and Mrs. Agassiz took Pauline with them, and Alexander and Ida remained in America.

Agassiz was elated at the thought of seeing his family and his beloved Alps and Jura once more.

"I am a Swiss," he had told someone recently. "My family has been Swiss for centuries, and in spite of my ten years' exile I am Swiss still."

Great Britain was their first European stop, and wherever they went prominent persons were waiting to welcome them. Many were old-time associates of Agassiz's, and many were eagerly meeting him for the first time. He regretted that Dr. Buckland was no longer among them. Dr. Buckland had died three years before. But Sir Charles Lyell was very much alive and most eager to chat with Agassiz. One of the out-

A Scientist of Two Worlds

standing bits of scientific gossip in England was the fact that Charles Darwin, living in the village of Downe, had completed his book and it was soon to be published. Sir Charles Lyell was enthusiastic about Darwin's theories insofar as he knew them, but Agassiz shook his head.

The Agassizes went to Paris for a week, and there the same welcome was repeated. Secretly Agassiz wished Cuvier were among the welcomers, and he had arrived just a few months too late to see Dr. Humboldt once more.

From Paris they went on to Switzerland, calling first on the aged Mrs. Agassiz in Montagny near the southern end of the Lake of Neuchâtel, not far from the towns she had known so well: Concise, Orbe, Môtier, Morat, and Neuchâtel. She was living with her daughter Cecile, now Mrs. Wagnon.

"Stay a while, my son," she pleaded. "This is probably the last time I shall see you."

They did. They stayed several weeks. From Montagny they went down to Lausanne to visit Agassiz's other sister, Olympe, now Mrs. Francillon. At last they went up to the nearby Diablerets Mountains to visit Auguste Agassiz. He was ill and resting at a health resort.

Meanwhile the Swiss scientific world had been bustling with excitement at the thought of having Louis Agassiz with them once more. The Helvetic Society sent out a notice of a special session to be held at the Conservatory of Music in Geneva on August 24 and 25. Agassiz was to be present! That was all the members needed to know. They came from nearly every canton to hear him speak.

The Agassizes visited the Mayor family in Neuchâtel and the Brauns in Germany before leaving Europe, and they arrived back in Boston the end of September.

"How is my museum?" was Louis Agassiz's first question on his return.

When Scientists Disagree

It was well under way, and before the end of the year he was able to start moving his collections from the wooden building into their new shelter and plan their arrangement. Some part of almost every day for the rest of his life, except when he was off on a scientific expedition, was given to the museum.

For the big task of transporting and arranging the collections, he enlisted the aid of his students, but it was difficult to hold the attention of young men during those times. Often he found their lack of interest in the museum discouraging, even though he understood it. In October, 1859, just a few days after Agassiz returned from Europe, an Abolitionist named John Brown had led a raid on Harper's Ferry, Virginia, to free some Negro slaves there. Brown was arrested and hanged, and the event increased the tension on every side. Young people were the most excitable of all.

Agassiz became involved in his own scientific excitement that same fall when he received a copy of the long-awaited book by Charles Darwin, *The Origin of Species by Means of Natural Selection*. Dr. Asa Gray received a copy at the same time. As outstanding scientists all over the world read Darwin's book, they began to take sides. Some were ardently in favor of his ideas; others were just as ardently opposed.

By *species* scientists then meant just about what the word means now. A species is a group of individual plants or animals that are essentially alike, differing from each other only in minor details. In Agassiz's day most zoologists agreed with Cuvier's system which divided the whole animal kingdom into four great parts: Radiates (those with radial symmetry), Mollusks (clams, oysters, snails), Articulates (insects, lobsters, crayfish), and Vertebrates (fishes, reptiles, birds, mammals). As a result of having more powerful microscopes and another whole century in which to do research, modern zoologists

A Scientist of Two Worlds

divide the animal kingdom into eleven principal parts, each of which is called a Phylum. The word *phylum* is from the Greek and means "race." (There is a chart in the back of the book which shows these eleven divisions. There are a few animal forms which have not yet been classified.) Each Phylum is divided into Classes. The Classes are divided into Orders; the Orders into Families; the Families into Genera; and the Genera into species. Latin and Greek words are always used, since they are standard the world over, and thus scientists will always know exactly what creature they are discussing no matter what their native language happens to be.

What puzzled scientists in Agassiz's and Darwin's day, and still puzzles them, was the question: why? Why are there so many species? How did new species happen? Agassiz had expressed his best ideas on this question in Part I of his *Contributions to the Natural History of the United States.* Then along came Darwin's *Origin of Species* that contained a new theory contrary to that of Agassiz's.

Just as Agassiz had opened a door to new areas of learning with his theory of an Ice Age, so did Darwin open a door to new thinking about species.

Darwin had spent years on research before he wrote his book, and in it he set forth his reasoning with the greatest care. The young, he said, are never exactly like their parents. There are always slight variations. A farmer will select the variations he likes best, to grow the next generation, and the next and the next, until he has just the kind of cow, horse, or chicken that he wants. Mother Nature does the same thing, only she is a lot crueler about it. Animals living in a wild state have a severe struggle for existence. They have all kinds of natural enemies. Only a few survive. The ones who survive have done so because they were the fittest.

Darwin gave many illustrations. There was the moth who clung to the bark of a tree. His color almost exactly matched the bark, and this helped him to escape capture by birds. Darwin maintained that once there had been ancestors of this fellow whose colors were brighter. But, when a variation occurred in the young, that is, when a moth developed whose color was safer, he had a better chance of surviving, laying eggs, and producing more like himself. The brighter moths were more easily found and eaten by the birds. In the far north, the animals with the whitest fur were safest from their enemies. Insects which fed on leaves were green in color. The same was true in the plant world. The fur on the peach discouraged the beetles, and so furry peaches survived. A plant could produce a great quantity of seeds, and only a few would survive to produce next year's plants. They were the fittest.

All plant and animal life, Darwin reasoned, is constantly changing and progressing. Over millions of years, natural selection has been at work, and is still at work. Mother Nature produces more of everything than she needs each season and selects the best from each generation.

Darwin had tremendous vision. It was possible that all life on the earth had begun from a single, simple form, he reasoned, and that all the species evolved from it. Today scientists are convinced of this principle. Life, they think, began with the single cell, in the water. Gradually, many-celled animals developed, and varied. Some found their way up on the land in the form of amphibians. From the amphibians the land animals developed: reptiles, birds, mammals, man.

Change is still going on; it will always go on, declared

A Scientist of Two Worlds

Darwin. There will always be new species occurring. Darwin could see that there was a great plan in nature and that all living things were related. Agassiz believed that there was a great plan, too, but his plan was different from Darwin's.

"The major types of animals are permanent," Agassiz insisted. "There may be some effect of evolution through natural selection, but it is very limited. This whole question of inheritance is exceedingly intricate."

He felt, from the observations he had made, that all the principal types of animals had existed since earliest geological times.

There has probably never been such a battle of words on any subject as there was on Darwin's theory of evolution. What enraged nonscientific people most was having to think that they could have any cousins among the brutes.

Such scientific men as Sir Charles Lyell and Dr. Asa Gray were strongly in favor of Darwin's theory. Darwin's chief opponent in America was Louis Agassiz. So deeply did both Dr. Gray and Dr. Agassiz feel about the matter that it ended their long friendship. It made both men, as well as all their mutual friends, unhappy. But an honest man must be true to his own convictions, no matter what the cost, and both Agassiz and Gray were honest men. So were Darwin, Lyell and all the other scientists who plunged into the controversy. They disagreed because information on the subject was incomplete; it still is.

But, even though we still don't know the whole story of life on the earth, we have learned a great deal since the days of the Darwin controversy. Today, most scientists accept Darwin's theory as an important part of the story of life. As paleontologists have explored the world and have dug into

When Scientists Disagree

likely places, they have found specimens of manlike creatures and primitive men which prove how man evolved from lower forms. The first true man probably appeared on the earth about one hundred and fifty thousand years ago. Before him there were more primitive types of men, and before them there were ape men. Only in recent years have the remains of the ape men been discovered in South Africa.

But what makes a new species happen? Why are the young not exactly like their parents? Why did an ape man occur? What caused higher forms of men to happen?

Where man is concerned, scientists are sure of this much: all human beings on the earth today are of the same species. Where all species are concerned, scientists are certain that spontaneous mutations do occur. That is, a new creature will appear that is noticeably different from its parents. Mutations are occurring all the time in the wild state of nature, but most of them disappear because they are not suited to their environment. When a new trait occurs that is particularly suited to its environment—a protective darker skin in the tropics where the sun is so hot, whiter fur in the land of perpetual snow, a longer neck where food is hard to reach—the trait helps the creature to survive better. Thus, he produces more of his kind, and the trait becomes more and more noticeable over the centuries.

Scientists are beginning to inquire into the effect of radioactivity. We do know that radiation affects the hereditary cells. A certain amount of radioactivity occurs in nature. Cosmic rays bombard us from outer space. Radioactive materials exist in the ground.

Origin of species is still a question for the future.

While the controversy over Darwin's book continued, so did another controversy in America: slavery. Out of the dif-

149

A Scientist of Two Worlds

ferences between the industrial North and the slave-holding South developed still another argument: secession. Many Southern states were threatening to secede from the Union. When the results of the Presidential election of November, 1860, were in, and the news reached South Carolina that Lincoln had been elected, South Carolina seceded. In only a few weeks ten other Southern states did the same.

Nothing made Agassiz sadder than to witness the fading interest of his students in their work. Those who were helping him at the new museum had to be supervised in everything they did. Their attention wandered and they made mistakes. Soon they themselves wandered—off to war.

The first guns to speak in the Civil War were fired April 12, 1861, on Fort Sumter, a federal island guarding the harbor of Charleston. There was no holding the young men after that. During the next four years all over America life was disturbed and filled with tragedy.

Agassiz had never liked guns, not even in his youngest and most adventuresome years. His hunting had been done with notebook and pencil. To him life was precious, something wonderful and mysterious that God had created, something that man could some day hope to comprehend. For men to destroy one another's lives in order to settle a political dispute seemed to him more primitive than the wild creatures of the forest. Wild creatures killed as a matter of instinct, but man had the power to reason. There was no excuse for man!

He shouldered most of the museum work himself along with the research and writing of his volumes on the natural history of the United States. Volume IV came out in 1862, but that was the last volume anyone saw. Agassiz was past his prime. He could no longer work as he had when he was twenty. The museum was requiring more of him than he had had any idea it would.

Mr. and Mrs. Agassiz spent their winters in Cambridge and their summers at Nahant, with Pauline and Ida and sometimes Alexander and his new wife, Anna Russell.

Alexander Agassiz had remained a teacher in his stepmother's school for girls just long enough to fall in love with one of his students. As soon as he realized that he wanted to marry, he knew he must search for a post with an adequate salary. He joined the Coast Survey and worked with Dr. Bache for a while. But when the Museum of Comparative Zoology was established, he was appointed, much to his father's joy, as its agent at a salary of fifteen hundred dollars a year. He and Anna Russell were married and moved into the big house on Quincy Street.

As for the girls' school, Elizabeth Agassiz continued it until the third year of the war and then decided not to keep it open any longer.

Elizabeth Agassiz had many, many occasions to reflect on her happiness during the years of her marriage with Louis Agassiz. She felt deeply happy to see father and son working so close together at the museum. How fortunate, she thought, that Alexander had followed in his father's footsteps. And it was very gratifying to her when her husband decided to become a citizen of the United States. His certificate came through in January, 1865. That same year the Royal Society in England bestowed the Copley Medal upon him. The Copley Medal is the highest honor that the Royal Society has to offer, and it is given for devotion to scientific experiment. Benjamin Franklin had received it in 1753 for his work with electricity.

Mrs. Agassiz knew that it was not honor and recognition

A Scientist of Two Worlds

that concerned this extraordinary husband of hers. He never thought of himself. He thought of science. He and his son Alexander were engrossed in the museum.

Both Louis and Alexander Agassiz knew that the collections at the museum were far from complete. They must go on diligently searching for collections that they could purchase, and diligently doing a great deal of collecting themselves. Very much alive in Louis Agassiz's memory were all the collecting trips he had ever taken. His most recent trip had been through Maine, looking for glacial evidence. He had followed for miles with a compass in his hand the streaks and markings on the rocks, to show how the glacier had advanced from Bangor to the seacoast. He had explored the Carolinas, the Mississippi River, and before that, Lake Superior. It did not seem possible that his Lake Superior trip had been sixteen years ago. Long before Lake Superior he had learned to know the Alps and the Jura like the palm of his own hand.

The collecting journey that lived most vividly in his heart was the one he had not really taken. That was the journey of Spix and Martius to Brazil. They had brought back to Europe so many hundreds of hitherto unknown species of fishes. The task of sorting out and classifying that huge collection of fishes had been Agassiz's first real opportunity as a young scientist.

A journey to Brazil! Well, why not?

"I *do* need a vacation," he said half aloud and half to himself. "Perhaps a quiet trip to Brazil . . ."

The idea grew little by little each day. Now that she was no longer tied to her school Mrs. Agassiz was delighted with the prospect of a journey to South America. The excitement in the Agassiz household built up.

One day Agassiz happened to be chatting with Mr. Na-

When Scientists Disagree

thaniel Thayer, a wealthy Bostonian and a member of the museum's Board of Trustees.

"I might spend the summer in Rio de Janeiro," Agassiz told Thayer.

"What a rover you are," the other replied.

"I am tired," said Agassiz. "I am going to loaf a little in Brazil."

At that his friend burst out laughing. "I can imagine how long you will loaf—perhaps a week or two. If you go, I think you had better prepare yourself for a collecting expedition."

"That is too expensive," said Agassiz.

Both men had the interest of the museum at heart. Both men knew how valuable a Brazilian collection would be, especially if collected by the expert Agassiz. Before very much longer Thayer had made plans to finance an expedition to Brazil for Professor and Mrs. Agassiz and six assistants. The whole thing was so obviously an excellent idea that the Pacific Mail Steamship Company offered the whole party free transportation on one of its passenger steamers, the *Colorado,* as far as Rio.

In March Louis Agassiz wrote a long letter to his mother in Switzerland.

"Dear Mother, you will shed tears of joy when you read this, but such tears are harmless. Listen, then, to what has happened . . ." and he told her the whole story, including every word of his conversation with Thayer. "My pleasure trip was transformed into an important scientific expedition for the benefit of the Museum. . . . I seem like the spoiled child of the country, and I hope God will give me strength to repay in devotion to her institutions and to her scientific and intellectual development, all that her citizens have done for me.

"I am forgetting that you will be anxious to know what

153

special work I propose to do in the interest of science in Brazil. First, I hope to make large collections of all such objects as properly belong in a Museum of Natural History. ... My only regret is that I must leave Alex in Cambridge to take care of the Museum itself. ... We leave next week."

12

A JOURNEY
IN BRAZIL

T HE *Colorado* sailed from New York on April 1, 1865. She was en route to the Pacific Coast by way of Cape Horn, and her passenger list included a party of sixteen adventurers headed for Rio. Agassiz's scientific group had expanded rapidly. Of course, Mrs. Agassiz was with him. He chose six staff members from the museum, each from a different department, including James Burkhardt who was still his artist, a conchologist, two geologists, and an ornithologist. To these he added six students, one of whom was William James, who later became the famous philosopher. Mrs. Agassiz's brother, Thomas Cary, went along as an assistant, and so did Dr. B. E. Cotting, a curator of the Lowell Institute, and Mrs. Cotting.

Elizabeth Cary Agassiz kept a daily diary of the voyage, and she began it the next day: "April 2, 1865, our first Sunday at sea. The weather is delicious, the ship as steady as anything on the water can be, and even the most forlorn of our party have little excuse for seasickness."

The second day out they were off shore from Petersburg, Virginia, and they noticed a great cloud of smoke rising from the city. Not until they reached Rio in the middle of May did they learn that the smoke had been the Battle of Petersburg in which General Grant captured the city. Just a week later General Lee had surrendered at Appomattox, bringing the Civil War to an end.

Professor Agassiz stood at the rail late that second day out, watching and taking notes.

"I want to observe the various temperatures of the Gulf Stream," he said.

The ship cut across the Gulf Stream opposite Cape Hatteras, about six in the evening and was past it by midnight. The temperature had been about 57°, but while they were in the Gulf Stream it rose to 74°, and as soon as they were out of the Gulf Stream the temperature dropped to 68°.

"Nature amazes me! She always will!"

During the three weeks from New York to Rio, Agassiz lectured to his staff nearly every day. He wanted them to be fully prepared for their tasks. Out of the dredging net one day he picked up a piece of common seaweed. Here was a simple form of plant life, an alga, called kelp. It was closely related to such simple land plants as yeast and lichens. Holding the plant up before his class, he explained each tiny animal clinging to it, showing how important kelp is to the life of the sea and how many animals depend upon it for both food and shelter.

Or, "Look at this flying fish!" he would say with as much joy as a small boy. "Did you think he could fly? He cannot. He simply dives into the air when he is escaping from big fishes that would eat him. He glides along on highly developed fins but he cannot flap them."

Glaciers had their turn, too, because Professor Agassiz was planning to search for evidence of an Ice Age in the southern hemisphere.

Now and then his lectures were spiced with a remark about Charles Darwin and the *Origin of Species*. "But the first inquiry is," he said one day, "how far are species distinct all over the world and what are their limits?" Then he added, "Until this is ascertained, all theories about their origin, their derivation from one another, their successive transformation, their migration from given centers, and so on, are mere beating about the bush."

When the *Colorado* reached the smooth, warm waters of the Caribbean, he told everyone to be on the lookout for jellyfish.

It was when he lectured on the fishes of South America that his group enjoyed him most. These were the creatures of the southern hemisphere about which he had learned so much from the Spix and Martius collection. He had done that research more than thirty-five years ago and the facts were still fresh in his mind. That was Agassiz for you!

On the twenty-third of April, Elizabeth Agassiz wrote in her diary: "Yesterday at early dawn we made Cape Frio light, and at seven o'clock were aroused by the welcome information that the Organ Mountains were in sight."

The *Colorado* steamed through a narrow, rocky passage into a wide blue expanse of water—the harbor of Rio de Janeiro.

"The Organ Mountains lift their singular needle-like points, while within the entrance rises the bare bleak rock so well known as the Sugar Loaf. . . . Once within this narrow rocky portal, the immense harbor, stretching northward for more than twenty miles, seems rather like a vast lake enclosed by mountains than like a bay. . . . We reached our anchorage at eleven o'clock. . . . The city of Rio de Janeiro spreads in a kind of crescent shape around the western side of the bay, its environs stretching out to a considerable distance along the beaches, and running up on to the hills behind."

Elizabeth patted her husband's hand as they stood at the ship's rail.

"Soon I shall meet the friendly Emperor," he said.

He had been exchanging letters with the Emperor of Brazil, Dom Pedro II. Since the Emperor was an amateur scientist, he was happy and eager to have a scientific investigation made of his country. The first thing that Agassiz did, once they were ashore, was to pay a call on the Emperor. The Emperor, with great fanfare and many escorts and much firing of salutes, returned the courtesy by paying a visit to the *Colorado*.

"Oh, he is a young man," Mrs. Agassiz observed, as the Imperial Yacht came alongside and the Emperor climbed aboard.

Dom Pedro II was dignified and genial, courteous and friendly. With great animation and enthusiasm he wanted to know all their plans, inspect their scientific gear, look at the specimens they had collected so far. For their trip up the Amazon, he promised them, they would have as a guide Major Coutinho, an officer of the Brazilian engineer corps, who had done a great deal of traveling in the Amazon regions and had even lived with the Indians.

"I shall write letters to you from all along the line," Agassiz promised in return.

A Journey in Brazil

Since the *Colorado* was continuing on around the Horn, Agassiz's party moved ashore and remained in Rio for three months. There they had the use of a big empty warehouse near the harbor, where Burkhardt could make colored drawings of fishes brought in by the fishing boats, and the other scientists could work at their tasks of dissecting, mounting skeletons, preserving other specimens in alcohol.

There was time for visiting the city of Rio and the countryside, too. Since they were special friends of the Emperor, they were invited everywhere.

Rio de Janeiro today is a beautiful, modern city, one of the loveliest in the world, but it was not so when the Agassizes were there. The streets were narrow and complicated, many of them unpaved, and yet it was picturesque. Its houses were stucco, painted in different colors, with fluted red tile roofs, and there were little balconies in front of the windows.

Very soon after their arrival the Agassizes hired a carriage and drove about the city, making slow progress through the crowded streets. They passed women with their heads wrapped in turbans and long bright-colored shawls gathered around their shoulders, padres in long coats and square hats, mules laden with baskets of fruit or vegetables, half-naked Negro carriers with heavy loads on their heads.

"Some of the Negroes appear to be slaves," said Agassiz.

"Yes, Professor," he was told. "There is slavery in Brazil still, but it will soon be finished. When it finishes in the United States, it will finish everywhere."

The Agassizes made many excursions out into the country. They spent a whole week at a coffee fazenda. The vegetation everywhere was tropical. Coconuts hung from tall palm trees; banana trees were filled with yellow fruit; brilliant red flowers hung from passion vines.

But Agassiz's biggest project in Brazil was to explore the Amazon River, and all the while he worked in Rio he was planning the excursion. On the twenty-fifth of July they all went aboard the *Cruzeiro do Sul,* and with them was the new member of their party, Major Coutinho.

The steamer proved to be small and crowded, and as they sailed northward up the coast of Brazil the water was choppy. Most of them felt half seasick during the trip, and they welcomed every stop that the *Cruzeiro do Sul* made. They were able to stay over night at Bahia, and make shorter visits at Maceió, Pernambuco, and Fortaleza.

The vivid blue of the ocean began to turn to a brownish-green.

"We are nearing the Amazon," Major Coutinho told them. "Its waters are a yellowish color and they change the color of the ocean for miles."

At last their steamer turned inland, to the mouth of the Amazon, and the city of Pará. Pará, much smaller than Rio, was mostly stucco buildings whitewashed or yellow-washed, with red tile roofs, and the land all about was flat. The air was hot and humid, because they were practically on the equator, in the real tropics, the land of the rubber tree and the dense, lush green jungles. A vulture or two soared overhead.

"The dry season began in June and will last through December," Major Coutinho explained. "But when it does come down, it rains twenty-five hours a day."

"And this mighty Amazon," said Agassiz, "with its hundreds of tributaries, carries all that rainfall out to the sea."

"It is the biggest river system in the world, Professor."

Again the officials of the city gave Agassiz the use of a big warehouse near the waterfront. Agassiz hurried back and

A Journey in Brazil

forth, back and forth, superintending the landing of their things.

"There are excellent workrooms for laboratories and storage of specimens, and cool chambers on the second floor where the men can sling their hammocks," he told his wife.

They had long since learned from the natives how to be comfortable at night. There were no beds or bedding. The Brazilians wove hammocks of palm fibres, and these were light to carry and proved cool and comfortable to sleep on. A hammock and a big piece of mosquito netting were all one needed.

Just as in Rio, Agassiz explored the country around Pará, and after only five days he had collected more than fifty new species of fresh-water fishes.

"These will undoubtedly improve our method of classifying fishes," he remarked.

Agassiz's mind was never closed, and his conclusions were never final. He sought all his life to improve his ideas and methods, and he did it by continually searching for more facts.

He kept each of his assistants as busy as he. In addition to the new specimens of fishes, he was working with his geologists to gather evidence of glaciers in Brazil. There was glacial drift all along the coast. Near Rio there had been erratic boulders, near Bahia the telltale shale and gravel, and he dug down into some sandstone near Pernambuco and came up with fossil shells to show that that region had once been under the sea. South America had as complicated a geological history as North America or Europe.

On August 20 the whole happy crowd of adventurers went aboard the river steamer, *Icamiaba,* to start the most exciting part of their voyage, the thousand-mile trek to Manaus, and many more miles beyond. There were so many legends about the interior of Brazil, its dense jungles, its primitive tribes, its man-eating crocodiles, its vampires, ocelots, jaguars, and anacondas, that everyone felt a real thrill as the steamer began to move westward.

The Amazon was still too wide for them to see the opposite shore. The Amazon was fantastic! It moved slowly, deeply.

"This river," said Professor Agassiz, "is not like a river. It seems more like the flow of an ocean."

The steamer took the Agassiz party past jungles, occasional clearings with a few thatched huts, past little towns like Breves and Monte Alegre.

"Note the many varieties of palm tree," said Agassiz. "That tall majestic fellow with its crown of plume-like leaves and its bunches of berry-like fruit just below the leaves, is the Assai palm. The Miriti is one of the most beautiful with its clusters of reddish fruit and its enormous, spreading, fanlike leaves."

They reached the town of Breves on their second day. It was a little colony of mud and thatch cottages scattered about without any streets. The population was very mixed. Some had Indian features, some Negro, some had very white skin and the coarse straight black hair of Indians.

The people of Breves crowded around the travelers trying to sell them little monkeys and bright-colored parrots and handmade pottery. But Professor Agassiz knew how to handle the situation. He made friends with the small boys in the village and set them to work bringing him snakes, fishes, and insects. Soon they learned that they could sell the learned travelers anything provided it was alive and different.

A Journey in Brazil

The travelers returned to their ship the same evening and were soon on their way again. The river had grown narrower, only a quarter of a mile across. They were still passing through dense forests that were sometimes more dense because of vines hung with pink and blue morning-glory blossoms, or they glided by swamps filled with tall grass where long-legged herons walked about. Agassiz marveled at the grandeur of the scenery every day. Palm trees were gradually disappearing and in their place were cotton trees with tall spreading tops, and mangabeira trees, leafless, hung with red seed pods, and mulatto trees with yellow bark and tiny white flowers among their dark-green leaves. The land seemed to be level plain for the first five days of the journey upriver, until the *Icamiaba* came to the hills of Almeirim.

"Martius landed here," said Agassiz. "He ascertained the height of these hills to be more than eight hundred feet above the river."

That evening the travelers sat on the upper front deck and watched a breath-taking sunset that turned the river crimson red and gradually faded to rose and pale pink.

When the adventurers reached Monte Alegre they found themselves in land that Mrs. Agassiz called "rather sombre; the soil consists everywhere of sand, the forest is low, while here and there intervene wide flats covered with coarse grass. The villagers depend for their livelihood on fishing and on growing cacao and India rubber."

After only a day at Monte Alegre they moved on to the next town, Villa Bella. Here Dr. Agassiz spent an afternoon visiting with Dr. Marcus, a local scientist who had sent him specimens from time to time, and with whom he had been exchanging letters.

Dr. Agassiz had brought along two South American canoes,

the kind that are flat with a dome-shaped cabin in the stern. He and Dr. Marcus explored the local tributary in one of them.

On the party sailed from Villa Bella, deeper and deeper into the wilds of Brazil, visiting strange Indian tribes in their thatched huts, watching them dance to the twanging music of primitive guitars, eating strange foods, accumulating hundreds of unknown species.

Life on the river itself seemed safe enough, but when they climbed into their canoes to explore tributaries, they felt the tension of being in a strange, unknown world, with forests woven into a dense wall on either side, their canoes gliding along in what Mrs. Agassiz called "shady narrow channels, mere boat paths through the forest." And deep amongst the trees they could hear the sounds of the wild life: chattering monkeys, screaming macaws.

They reached Manaus on the fourth of September. "Yesterday morning we entered the Rio Negro," Mrs. Agassiz wrote, "and saw the meeting of its calm, black waters with the rushing yellow current of the Upper Amazon."

The Rio Negro was one of the big tributaries of the Amazon, flowing southward from Venezuela and Colombia. Manaus was about six miles up the Rio Negro, on a high elevation of the bank. The river level changed nearly fifty feet between the dry and wet seasons. When the Agassizes arrived, the town perched high above the water, but during the rainy season it would stand almost at river level.

Manaus seemed remarkably comfortable and civilized after all the primitive life the travelers had seen along the way. The town then was just a collection of houses, some of them rather tumble-down, but Manaus was a commercial center just the same. That was as far as deep-water boats could go

A Journey in Brazil

up the Amazon system, and it was the shipping point for the crude rubber of the local rubber plantations.

The scientific party had been expected. A crowd hurried down to the pier to welcome them, and an official assured them that a house was being made ready.

As Agassiz looked around he could see forest in almost every direction, filled with God's creatures, filled with Mother Nature's secrets. The steamer would not be leaving for the Upper Amazon for a whole week, and he was delighted at the chance to linger here in this town buried so deep in the wild country. The other passengers were glad for a rest ashore, too.

During the week Mrs. Agassiz did her own kind of exploring. She made friends with the people of the town. She visited an Indian school just outside of Manaus and was astonished at the crafts the Indian children were learning: furniture making, ironwork, weaving. The scene she liked best happened every evening at nightfall in Manaus:

"One of my greatest pleasures in Manaus has been to walk toward the neighboring forest at nightfall, and see the water carriers, Indian and Negro, coming down from the narrow pathways with their great red earthen jars on their heads. They make quite a procession at morning and evening; for the river water is not considered good, and the town is chiefly supplied from pools and little streamlets in the woods. Many of these pools, very prettily situated and embowered in trees, are used as bathing places."

On the twelfth of September they boarded the steamer once more, and they were soon gliding upstream, beginning a six-weeks' exploration of the Upper Amazon, the portion of the Amazon often called the Solimões River. They stopped at towns and villages with storybook names: Coari,

Teffé, Tabatinga. As they traveled westward the forest grew less dense; the shore line rose higher with red cliffs; turtles and alligators abounded. Peru and the Andes were ahead of them. The river became narrower and shallower.

Tabatinga was their westernmost point, and they did not reach it until the twentieth of September.

"Tabatinga is the frontier town between Brazil and Peru," Mrs. Agassiz jotted down, "and is dignified by the name of a military station, though when one looks at the two or three small mounted guns on the bank, the mud house behind them constituting barracks, with half a dozen soldiers lounging in front of it, one cannot but think that the fortification is not a very formidable one. The town itself standing on a mud bluff, deeply ravined and cracked in many directions, consists of some dozen ruinous houses built around an open square."

The travelers could not dally long, since the "winter" was almost over, and soon the season of torrential rains would begin.

"Hurry! Hurry!" Professor Agassiz would say to his workers. "Do all you can."

As soon as their Brazilian steamer had loaded its cargo onto a Peruvian steamer that would take it on up the river into Peru, the return journey began.

"We will be delaying at Teffé," said Agassiz to his wife, with a grin.

She was as happy about it as he. Her first impression of Teffé on the way up had been that it was "the most smiling and pleasant" town they had seen in Brazil.

They were getting very close to the end of the dry season, though, and the Amazon was at its lowest. The steamer had to pick its way carefully. When they were almost at Teffé, the steamer gave a quick shudder and stopped and her motors went dead. Everyone rushed to the rail to see what was the matter. The steamer was aground in the mud. They had to wait several hours for a rainfall that would float her off. Around five in the evening the sky darkened and a rain squall soon released the boat. It did more. It warned the travelers that this was the kind of weather they could begin to expect.

They almost forgot to worry about the seasons when they reached Teffé once more. It was just as charming as they had remembered it. The village stood above a broad, sandy beach, and its houses were of mud and roofed with tiles, or thatched with palm. Around almost every house there was a plot of cultivated land and a picket fence, and inside the fence stood orange and palm trees. Behind the town rose a sloping green hill where cows and sheep grazed.

Agassiz rubbed his hands together as he looked at the many little inlets and lakes where he was going to take excursions in one of his canoes.

Fish and turtles were the two big products of Teffé, especially turtle eggs from which the people of Teffé made a kind of turtle butter. Everyone in the party knew the story of Agassiz's turtle eggs—just three hours old and no older—that had been rushed to him by a determined young teacher riding a Sunday freight train.

"There will be turtle eggs of every state of development for you here, Professor!" someone chided him.

"Ah, yes!" he agreed and chuckled.

The steamer let them remain at Teffé until the third week in October, and when at last they prepared to go aboard once more, Mrs. Agassiz just smiled and shook her head when she saw the stack of barrels and boxes full of specimens the

A Scientist of Two Worlds

men had collected—more than thirty.

"I have just taken my last ramble in the woods where I have had so many pleasant walks," she jotted down in her diary. "And now we are sitting in the midst of valises and carpet-bags, waiting to close this chapter of our Amazonian life."

It was raining when they finally were all aboard the *Icamiaba*. Each evening lately had brought a flashing, crashing thunderstorm.

When they reached Manaus, a happy surprise awaited them. The government of Brazil had placed a steamer at their disposal—the *Ibicuhy*—which meant that they did not have to depend upon the scheduled commercial steamers.

On the way up the Amazon Agassiz had expressed an ambition to explore the Rio Negro that flows into the Amazon near Manaus. Having a private steamer made it possible.

First, though, he explored every nook and cranny of the region around Manaus. He and his party found Indian villages of thatched huts, watched the Indians hunt for fish and turtles, or make farinha or tapioca, or dry and roll tobacco, or dance on their festival days. In the village of Mauhes, stretching along the high grassy river bank, the Indians wore the typical dress of the primitive Brazilians: a long straight piece of cotton with a hole for the head, hanging before and behind, and fastened with a belt, and a rough straw hat. But at Mucaja-Tuba the Indians wore more modern dress; the men wore trousers and shirts while the women went about in full calico skirts and blouses with their long, thick, black hair fastened high on their heads with combs. The Mundurucu Indians went half naked, the upper parts of their bodies covered with tattoo designs.

Mr. and Mrs. Agassiz stood together at the rail of the

168

A Journey in Brazil

Ibicuhy, as they began their exploration up the Rio Negro. They were beginning to have frequent rainstorms and the air was often cool and comfortable. They were grateful for the relief from so much heat and humidity.

"I'm really becoming accustomed to this fascinating country," said Elizabeth Agassiz.

"Even the insects?" he teased.

"Well . . ."

Mosquitoes, gnats, cockroaches that swarmed everywhere, ants, were all part of a traveler's lot in tropical Brazil. On the cruise up the Rio Negro Mrs. Agassiz wrote down her thoughts on this aspect of Brazil:

"I must confess the creature who greeted my waking sight one morning was not a pleasant object to contemplate. It was an enormous centipede close by my side, nearly a foot in length, whose innumerable legs looked just ready for a start, and whose two horns or feelers were protruded with a most venomous expression. These animals are not only hideous to look upon, but their bite is very painful, although not dangerous."

That time, she slipped away from her visitor without disturbing him, and told the world of science about him. He was soon deposited in a jar of alcohol.

Another time: "I shake out my dress, and I hear a cold flop on the floor, and a pretty little house-lizard, who has found a warm retreat in its folds, makes his escape."

And again: "I remember once, having hung some towels to dry on the cord of my hammock; I was about to remove them, when suddenly my hand and arm seemed plunged in fire. I dropped the towels as if they had been hot coals, which for the moment they literally seemed to be, and then I saw that my arm was covered with little brown ants.

A Scientist of Two Worlds

Brushing them off in all haste, I called Laudigari, who found an army of them passing over the hammock, and out of the window, near which it hung. He said they were on their way somewhere, and, if left undisturbed, would be gone in an hour or so." They had been "fire-ants."

When at last the cruise up the Rio Negro was ended, and the scientists returned to Manaus at the end of December, Louis Agassiz was ready to collapse from fatigue. He had come to South America to build up his health, and in many ways the out-of-door life had helped him. But he was a Swiss, and he didn't really have a tropical constitution. In addition, he had overworked continuously because he so earnestly wanted to accomplish as much as possible. Agassiz was tired enough to consent to a week of rest at Manaus before going the rest of the way down the Amazon to Pará.

But he had won as many friends and admirers in Brazil as he had ever won anywhere else, and when the citizens of Pará learned that they must say farewell, they begged him to give them a talk on the geology of the Amazon valley. He consented, and a meeting was arranged as soon as he reached Pará. Nearly two hundred persons came to hear his lecture, and as Louis Agassiz found himself in front of a class full of students eager to learn, he forgot his fatigue, forgot everything, except the desire to share his newest knowledge with them.

"The existence of a glacial period, however much derided when first announced, is now a recognized fact," he began, "and after my recent journey in the Amazon valley, I am led to add a new chapter to the strange history of glacial phenomena, taken from the southern hemisphere, and even from the tropics themselves."

He described all the geological observations he had made

A Journey in Brazil

in Brazil and told his audience of some he had made in North America.

"Throughout this whole tract of country the drift may be seen along the roadside, in immediate contact with the native crystalline rock. The fertility of the land, also, is a guide to the presence of drift. Wherever it lies thickest over the surface, there are the most flourishing coffee plantations. . . . No doubt the fertility arises from the great variety of chemical elements contained in the drift, and the kneading process it has undergone beneath the gigantic ice plough."

When at last he had finished his lecture, his audience crowded around him in great animation; they did not want to let him leave.

Departures had to be made, though, first at Pará, and later at Rio. The boat trip from Pará to Rio was made in a continuous downpour of rain.

Everyone in the party had worked hard—for three months in Rio, ten months in the Amazon valley, and another two months in the central and southern regions of Brazil—and everyone welcomed the weeks of rest aboard the ship that finally brought them home.

"I leave Brazil with great regret," Agassiz wrote to his mother while they were en route home. He had learned much, he told her, especially about glaciers and fishes. "A great part of this success is due to the unusual facilities granted me by the Brazilian government. . . . To the Emperor of Brazil I owe the warmest gratitude. . . ."

13

"MY MUSEUM"

THERE was a great flurry of happiness when the Agassizes returned to Cambridge. Tickets to the Lowell Institute were sold out weeks in advance of his first lecture on Brazil.

"I have been able to bring back so much for my museum!" he told his associates.

The Museum of Comparative Zoology had long since become the most important task in Agassiz's life, and he set to work at once on the mass of specimens from Brazil. He was deeply gratified to receive a letter of praise from the now aged Professor Martius, living in Munich. "You will easily believe that I followed your journey on the Amazons with the greatest interest," said the letter.

In the fall of 1867 Agassiz received word that his eighty-four-year-old mother had died, and he felt the loss quite keenly. She, more than anyone else, had had faith in his

"My Museum"

ability from his earliest years.

His own energies were going downhill. At times he felt downright frustrated when he could not do as much in a day as he wished. One day he felt so poorly that he strolled over to Longfellow's study to tell him of his despair.

"I cannot work," he said to Longfellow, and sinking into a chair buried his face in his hands and began to cry.

Longfellow did his best to comfort Agassiz.

Throughout the winter, Agassiz drove himself, and words of warning from those who loved him did no good. Towards spring he began to find it difficult to hold his hand steady when he wrote, and very soon afterward he collapsed and had to be put to bed.

"His heart has been affected," said the doctor. "He must have complete rest."

It was the hardest thing in the world for a man like Agassiz to do, but Mrs. Agassiz did manage to keep him away from his beloved work for several weeks. By summer he was able to take an excursion with some friends through the prairie regions of the West. On the way home he stopped at Ithaca, New York, for three months. Cornell University had just been incorporated and planned to open in 1868. Agassiz accepted a post as a nonresident professor.

He spent the spring of 1869 on a cruise along the coast of Cuba with Pourtelès who was with the Coast Survey.

But during the winter of 1870 he suffered another attack. This time he had to spend several months doing absolutely nothing.

"Oh, my museum! My museum!" he cried. "Always uppermost, by day and by night, in health and in sickness, always—always!"

He was determined to recover, and by summer he was able

173

A Scientist of Two Worlds

to get about with great caution. He knew, and everyone else knew, that he would never be a hearty, vigorous, well man again. But his spirit was as vigorous as ever, and his brilliant mind could still produce new ideas.

Louis Agassiz actually went on a long sea voyage in December of the year 1871. The ship was the *Hassler*, making an expedition for the United States Coast Survey. Agassiz and a whole group of naturalists were invited to go. Agassiz was glad to have Pourtalès with him once more, and happy that Mrs. Agassiz could accompany him. Again she kept a detailed diary of the journey, and watched her husband as well, to make certain that he did not overexert himself.

The *Hassler* made her way down to the Caribbean, to the West Indies, and then to Rio for three weeks. The dredging net was busy bringing in specimens almost every day. From Rio the *Hassler* went on to Montevideo, through the Straits of Magellan, and up the western coast of South America.

The weeks at sea were restful and restoring for Agassiz. He felt so well that he and Elizabeth Agassiz left the ship at Concepción, Chile, so that he could collect glacial evidence, and they rejoined the vessel at Valparaiso.

The ship cruised on out to the Galapagos, where Darwin had made so many observations on the wild life, and from the Galapagos sailed for Panama, then on up to San Diego Bay, arriving the middle of August.

The Agassizes went ashore at San Francisco and found themselves confronted with an old, old problem: Louis Agassiz's popularity. Everyone wanted to hear him speak. He did what he could, but that was not very much, because every speaking engagement taxed his strength to the utmost. After a month in San Francisco, he and Mrs. Agassiz returned

"My Museum"

home—with 265 barrels and cases of new specimens—for his museum.

Amazing though it may seem, Agassiz had one more contribution to make to American education. Before setting out in the *Hassler*, he had mentioned an idea to some of his Cambridge friends: a summer school for science teachers. When he returned, he found that the idea was already under way.

Not only was the idea of a summer school new, but his classes were to be for both men and women. Something almost unheard of!

Soon he was announcing definite plans for his summer school, a course in Natural Science for teachers and student-teachers, to meet for its first session on Nantucket Island. When the wealthy New Yorker, John Anderson, read of Agassiz's plan, he was so impressed that he offered Agassiz Penikese Island and fifty thousand dollars to operate his summer school on a permanent basis. Penikese Island is one of the Elizabeth Islands in Buzzard's Bay, between Martha's Vineyard and the coast of Massachusetts.

"It seems to me impossible to do otherwise than accept the great gift you offer," Agassiz wrote to Mr. Anderson. "It changes at once an experiment without fixed location or stable foundation into a permanent school for the study of nature, such as the world has not seen before. . . ."

The summer school was to be named the Anderson Summer School of Natural Science.

Forty-four persons, sixteen of them women, enrolled for that first course. Most of them were science teachers, except for one or two staff members from the Museum of Comparative Zoology, Count de Pourtalès, Arnold Guyot and Mrs. Agassiz.

A Scientist of Two Worlds

There were some buildings of an old farm on Penikese, and these became the school buildings. The barn was turned into the dining and lecture hall, and a new building was put up for the dormitory.

Actually the students arrived before the place was completely in order, but, like their teacher, they had come for learning. Another generous Bostonian had given the project a small yacht, so that the students could go out and dredge the sea for specimens.

At first glance, Agassiz seemed as ruddy and rugged as ever. But as he lectured to his students in the converted barn, or walked along the shore with them, or went out in the yacht, his companions could see that he was working with great effort.

"He is driving himself beyond his strength," said one.

"Yes," agreed another, "but what can you do? Give Professor Agassiz a group of students and he must teach."

He tried to teach them everything the island had to offer. The whole chain of islands was part of a terminal moraine left by some bygone glacier. Penikese was full of plant and bird life. The waters that lapped around its rocky inlets teemed with tiny creatures. The seas beyond held bigger forms.

"Strive to interpret what really exists," Professor Agassiz urged his students. "Search for the truth."

By the end of the summer Agassiz was obviously very, very tired, and his tall figure was stooped.

"You must rest," Elizabeth Agassiz insisted, "before you return to the museum."

Louis Agassiz consented, and he did rest for a full two weeks. But after that, no one could keep him away from his museum. He actually began a new course of lectures there—on radiates.

"My Museum"

On the second of December he journeyed to Fitchburg, Massachusetts, to deliver a special lecture on domesticated animals.

"Those who accompanied him," Mrs. Agassiz wrote later, "and knew the mental and physical depression which had hung about him for weeks, could not see him take his place on the platform without anxiety. And yet, when he turned to the blackboard, and, with a single sweep of the chalk, drew the faultless outline of an egg, it seemed impossible that anything could be amiss with the hand or the brain that were so steady and so clear."

After the lecture, though, he began to complain of fading eyesight.

"I feel strangely asleep," he said.

On the sixth he declared himself too weary to go out, and that was the last the world saw of Louis Agassiz and the last it ever heard of his brilliant lectures.

Late in the evening on the fourteenth of December, 1873, he died, and was buried four days later at nearby Mount Auburn Cemetery.

Louis Agassiz had achieved enough in his life to do credit to several men. He had made great contributions to the progress of science in both Europe and America. Medals, prizes, memberships in learned societies, were bestowed upon him by almost every country in the world. And yet, one of his favorite mottoes was:

Never be afraid to say, "I do not know."

THE END

PRINCIPAL GROUPINGS (*PHYLA*) OF THE ANIMAL KINGDOM USED BY PRESENT-DAY SCIENTISTS

1. Protozoa
   (*one-celled animals*) . . Amoebae, Paramecia
2. Porifera . . . . Sponges
3. Coelenterates . . . . . Jellyfishes, sea anemones, corals
4. Ctenophors . . . . . Sea walnuts
5. Platyhelminthes
   (*flatworms*) . . . . . Liver-flukes, tapeworms
6. Nemathelminthes
   (*roundworms*) . . . . Hookworms, trichinella
7. Echinoderms . . . . . Starfishes, sea urchins, sea cucumbers, sea lilies
8. Annelids
   (*segmented worms*) . . Earthworms, leaches
9. Mollusks . . . . . . Snails, slugs, clams, oysters, squids
10. Arthropods . . . . . Crayfishes, crabs, shrimps, lobsters, barnacles, water fleas, spiders, centipedes, scorpions, insects
11. Chordates
    Subphylum: Vertebrates (*creatures with backbones*):
    Class:
    Cyclostomes . . . . Lampreys
    Elasmobranchs
    (*cartilaginous fishes*) Sharks, rays, skates

179

A Scientist of Two Worlds

GROUPINGS OF ANIMAL KINGDOM (*continued*)

Osteichthyes
(*bony fishes*)
Subclass: *Lobe-fin*
fishes . . . . Lung fishes
Subclass: *Ray-fin*
fishes . . . . Most modern fishes (includes
Teleosts)
Amphibians. . . . Frogs, toads, and salamanders
Reptiles . . . . . Turtles, tortoises, crocodiles, al-
ligators, chameleons, lizards,
snakes
Aves . . . . . . Birds
Mammals. . . . . All animals that suckle their
young and have hair

WHERE YOUR FAMILY CAT BELONGS IN THE ANIMAL
KINGDOM:
Phylum: Chordates
Subphylum: Vertebrates
Class: Mammals
Order: Carnivors (flesh eating)
Family: Felines (pumas, lions, tigers, jaguars,
leopards, cougars, cheetahs, domestic
cats)
Genus: Felis
Species: domestica

WHERE MAN BELONGS IN THE ANIMAL KINGDOM:
Phylum: Chordates
Subphylum: Vertebrates
Class: Mammals
Order: Primates (with "nails" and a large brain)
Suborder: Anthropoids
Family: Hominids
Genus: Homo
Only one species: mankind

BIBLIOGRAPHY

AGASSIZ, ELIZABETH CARY. *Louis Agassiz, His Life and Correspondence.* Boston: Houghton Mifflin Company, 1885.

AGASSIZ, G. R. *Letters and Recollections of Alexander Agassiz.* Boston: Houghton Mifflin Company, 1913.

AGASSIZ, LOUIS. *A Journey in Brazil.* Boston: Ticknor and Fields, 1868.

———. *Lake Superior: Its Physical Character, Vegetation, and Animals, Compared with Those of Other and Similar Regions. With a Narrative of the Tour by J. Elliott Cabot.* Boston: Gould, Kendall, 1850.

———. *Narrative of an Expedition from Boston Through the Straits of Magellan to San Francisco in the Steamer Hassler.* Smithsonian Miscellaneous Collections, Volume 18.

ARTHUR, RICHARD. *Ten Thousand Miles in a Yacht.* New York: E. P. Dutton & Co., Inc., 1906.

BACON, EDWIN M. *Boston Illustrated.* Boston: Houghton Mifflin Company, 1893.

BAITY, ELIZABETH CHESLEY. *America Before Man.* New York: The Viking Press, 1953.

BEATTIE, WILLIAM. *Switzerland.* London: George Virtue, 1836.

CAIN, A. J. *Animal Species and Their Evolution.* London: Hutchinson & Co., Ltd., 1954.

CARRINGTON, RICHARD. *The Story of Our Earth.* New York: Harper & Brothers, 1956.

COOPER, LANE. *Louis Agassiz as a Teacher.* Ithaca: The Comstock Press, 1917.

COXE, WILLIAM. *Travels in Switzerland in the Country of the Grisons.* Basil: James Decker, 1802.

181

A Scientist of Two Worlds

DARWIN, CHARLES. *The Origin of Species by Means of Natural Selection.* New York: D. Appleton and Company, 1872.

FOUNTAIN, PAUL. *The River Amazon from Its Source to the Sea.* London: Constable & Company, Ltd., 1914.

FOWLE, OTTO. *Sault Ste. Marie and Its Great Waterway.* New York: G. P. Putnam's Sons, 1925.

GOS, CHARLES. *L'Hôtel des Neuchâtelois, Un Épisode de la Conquête des Alpes.* Lausanne: Librarie Payot et Cie., 1928.

GRAY, ASA. *Letters of Asa Gray.* (Edited by Jane Loring Gray) Boston: Houghton Mifflin Company, 1893.

GRIFFITHS, A. B. *Biographies of Scientific Men.* London: A Sutton, 1912.

GUYOT, ARNOLD. *Biographical Memoir of Louis Agassiz.* Biographical Memoirs Volume 2 of The National Academy of Sciences, 1886.

HATCHER, HARLAN. *The Great Lakes.* New York: Oxford University Press, 1944.

HEADLEY, J. T. *Letters from Italy.* New York: Baker and Scribner, 1848.

HOPPUS, JOHN. *The Continent in 1835.* London: Saunders and Otley, 1836.

JORDAN, DAVID STARR. *The Days of a Man.* Cleveland: World Book Company, 1922.

LAGLER, KARL F. *Freshwater Fishery Biology.* Dubuque: W. C. Brown Co., 1956.

LEE, MRS. R. *Memoirs of Baron Cuvier.* London: Longman, Rees, Orme, Brown, Green & Longman, 1833.

LONGFELLOW, HENRY. *Life of Henry Wadsworth Longfellow.* (Edited by Samuel Longfellow) Boston: Ticknor and Fields, 1886.

LYELL, SIR CHARLES. *Principles of Geology.* New York: D. Appleton and Company, 1872.

——. *A Second Visit to the United States of North America.* New York: Harper & Brothers, 1849.

——. *Travels in North America in the Years 1841-42.* New York: Wiley & Halsted, 1845.

Bibliography

MARCOU, JULES. *Life, Letters, and Works of Louis Agassiz.* New York: Macmillan and Co., 1896.

MOORE, RUTH. *Charles Darwin.* New York: Alfred A. Knopf, 1954.

———. *The Earth We Live on.* New York: Alfred A. Knopf, 1956.

———. *Man, Time, and Fossils.* New York: Alfred A. Knopf, 1953.

MORISON, SAMUEL ELIOT. *Three Centuries of Harvard.* Cambridge: Harvard University Press, 1936.

NUTE, GRACE LEE. *Lake Superior.* New York: The Bobbs-Merril Company, 1944.

PATON, LUCY ALLEN. *Elizabeth Cary Agassiz.* Boston: Houghton Mifflin Company, 1919.

PINCHER, CHAPMAN. *A Study of Fish.* New York: Duell, Sloan and Pearce, 1948.

RUSSELL, JOHN. *A Tour in Germany.* Edinburgh: Archibald Constable and Co., 1825.

SCHWARZENBERG, F. A. *Alexander von Humboldt.* London: Robert Hardwicke, 1866.

SMITH, B. WEBSTER. *The World in the Past.* London: Frederick Warne & Co., 1953.

WARD, HENSHAW. *Charles Darwin, The Man and His Warfare.* New York: The Bobbs-Merrill Company, 1927.

WEIMER, BERNAL R. *Man and the Animal World.* New York: John Wiley & Sons, Inc., 1951.

WILLIAMS, MEADE C. *Early Mackinac.* New York: Duffield & Company, 1912.

WOOD, EDWIN O. *Historic Mackinac.* New York: The Macmillan Company, 1918.

Magazine Articles:

The Scientific Monthly:

CORNISH, LOUIS C. "Agassiz's School on Penikese, Seventy Years After." October, 1943.

JORDAN, DR. DAVID STARR. "Louis Agassiz, Teacher." November, 1923.

INDEX

Aar glacier, 63, 73, 78-85, 94
Aar (river and valley), 63, 73, 78-85
Academy of Sciences, France, 131
Agassiz, Alexander (son), 60, 61, 80, 83, 86, 90-91, 93, 102, 124-125, 128, 129, 132, 134-135, 140, 143, 150-152, 154
Agassiz, Anna Russell, 151
Agassiz, Auguste (brother), 9-10, 12, 13, 14, 15-16, 17, 18-21, 28, 31, 37, 144
Agassiz, Cecile (sister), 14, 30, 144
Agassiz, Cecile Braun (first wife), 25, 26, 39, 40, 52-53, 61, 70, 77, 80, 82, 86, 93, 94, 102, 123
Agassiz, Elizabeth Cary (second wife), 126-128, 131-132, 133, 134-135, 143, 173, 174-177; school for young girls, 134-135, 151
Agassiz, Ida (daughter), 69, 86, 90, 124, 128, 133, 134-135, 143, 151
Agassiz, Louis (father), 11, 13, 21, 31-32, 33, 38, 70
Agassiz, Olympe (sister), 14, 144
Agassiz, Pauline (daughter), 86, 90, 124, 128, 133, 143, 151
Agassiz, Rose Mayor (mother), 10, 11-12, 27, 32, 71, 131, 144, 153, 172
Alcott, Bronson, 103, 141
Alps, 11, 19, 64, 66, 72-85, 143; Bernese, 20, 63, 71, 73; Tyrolean, 29
Amazon River system, 158, 160-170
America, 33, 59, 66, 88, 91, 97 f.
Ammonite, 50
Anderson Summer School of Natural Science, 175-176
Atomic theory, 65

Bache, Dr. Alexander, 100, 129, 151
Bex, 18, 55, 61-63, 75
Bienne, 14-15
Black fly, 118
Bonaparte, Charles (Prince of Canino), 88, 89, 92
Boston, 59, 95 f.
Braun, Alexander, 23-26, 27, 29, 33-34, 36, 37, 40, 45-46, 102, 123, 144
Braun, Cecile (wife), *see* Agassiz, Cecile
Braun, Emmy, 25, 82-83
Braun, Maximilian, 25, 71
Brazil, 30, 152-154, 155-171
Brazilian fishes, 31, 34-35, 158-171
British Association, 59
Buckland, Dr. William, 56-57, 83, 143
Buffalo, 110, 111
Burkhardt, Jacques, 127, 131, 155, 159

Cabot, J. Elliott, 108
Cambridge, 102, 103, 104 f., 172
Canada, 96, 108, 110, 120-122
Canino, Prince of, *see* Bonaparte
Cary, Thomas, 140
Cary, Thomas, Jr., 155
Chamonix (valley and village), 75
Charleston, 101, 131-132, 150
Charpentier, Jean de, 18, 55, 58, 61-63, 66, 75, 77
Christinat, Charles ("Papa"), 38-39, 100, 105, 122, 125, 126, 127
Civil War, 150, 156
Cleveland, 111
Col de Balme, 75
Colorado, 153, 155, 157, 159
Concise, 38, 71

185

Index

186

Index

187

Index